KU-681-041

developed to address the emerging issues. It was considered important to adopt an approach that would not only allow a number of different questions to be explored in separate projects, but also for the learning to be coherent and accessible to others. The collective projects evolved into the Joint Venture between the HEA and OPM, which ran from mid-1995 to mid-1996.

The four projects were designed to use a range of developmental approaches, work with different groups, and address different elements of the challenges raised by Chameleon and confirmed in the follow-up work. The projects addressed different ways of improving the commissioning and delivery of health services, particularly in the areas of health promotion and inequalities in health. In addition, the overall intention was to develop a network of interested and committed people, including a group within the HEA who would continue to develop the learning into practical guidance. This would enable the HEA to be part of a constantly extending and influential field development programme.

The four projects were as follows:

Roundabout

Carried out in partnership with the NHS Executive in the West Midlands, Roundabout was a behavioural simulation which explored how health gain and health promotion activity would fare in a primary care-led NHS

Research – health promotion and health gain in primary care

This project involved a series of discussions and interviews with GPs and other members of primary health-care teams to assess their involvement with health promotional activity in both their commissioning and provider roles, and their potential contribution to health gain.

Action learning sets

Thirty experienced managers and professionals from a wide range of commissioning backgrounds and organisations took part in action learning sets, which were designed to examine the extent to which they could collectively improve the commissioning process to achieve real improvements in health, and to explore the role of health promotion in these processes.

The health gain consultancy programme

This learning programme was for senior and experienced health promotion specialists. The 15 participants were drawn nationwide from both purchasers and providers. The programme explored new ways of managing and influencing the health promotion agenda in a primary care-led, devolved and evidence-driven NHS, oriented towards partnership.

Implementing the four projects in parallel provided opportunities to identify learning between and across the projects. The main forum where this took place was a workshop for all Joint Venture participants, held in May 1996, at which presentations on learning and implementation were made by those involved in each of the projects.

HAROLD BRIL
S. MARTIN'S COLLEGE
LANCASTER

0132689

T253
1070
HJH P
(Hea)

HAROLD BRIDGES LIBRARY
S. MARTIN'S COLLEGE
LANCASTER

ACHIEVING HEALTH GAIN

SEVEN DAY LOAN

This book is due for return on or before the last date shown below.

CANCELLED
24 JAN 2001   16 FEB 2006

13 MAR 2001   14 AUG 2006

9 MAR 2001

CANCELLED

22   2001   18 JAN 2008

20 1-9)

26   26 AP

19 JA   10. 5
        14 NOV

28 A   19 JAN

Don Gresswell Ltd., London,

DG 02242/71

CANCELLED

0752107194

ACHIEVING HEALTH GAIN

through **HEALTH PROMOTION**

in a **PRIMARY CARE-LED NHS**

Acknowledgements

We would like to thank all those who took part in the Joint Venture but especially:

The Joint Venture team: Anju Bhabuta, Helen Brown, Robin Douglas, Bernie Evans, Karen Ford, Ian Gee, Jeff Rodrigues and Jean Spray, and:
Victor Adebewobele, David Albury, Kathy Elliot, Jane Greenoak, Liz Haggard, Dominic Harrison, Christine Kent, Jane Lethbridge, Paul Lincoln, Diana McInnes, Laurie McMahon, Ged Maran, Peter Martin, Antony Morgan, Simon Sandberg, Marcia Saunders, Howard Shaw, Julia Unwin, and Dawn Waterman.

A list of participants in each of the Joint Venture projects is given in the Appendix.

© Health Education Authority, 1997

ISBN 0 7521 0719 4

First published 1997

Health Education Authority
Hamilton House
Mabledon Place
London WC1H 9TX

All rights reserved. No part of this publication may be reproduced in any material form (including photocopying or storing it in any medium by electronic means and whether or not transiently or incidentally to some other use of this publication) without the prior written permission of the copyright owner, except in accordance with the provisions of the Copyright, Designs and Patents Act 1988 or under the terms of a licence issued by the Copyright Licensing Agency, 90 Tottenham Court Road, London W1P 9HE. Applications for the copyright owner's permission to reproduce any part of this publication should be addressed in the first instance to the publisher.

Designed by Edwin Belchamber
Typeset by Wayzgoose
Printed in Great Britain

Contents

Foreword

This publication describes the programme of work undertaken by the Health Education Authority and Office for Public Management under the heading of the 'Joint Venture' during 1995 and 1996. The Joint Venture approach was chosen to reflect the commitment of both organisations to improving the real returns from investment in health – more commonly expressed as health gain.

The choices facing those involved in planning and commissioning health services are increasingly demanding – with more pressures and higher expectations in all areas of health, and real limitations on the resources available, the challenge is to invest in those services that can produce proven gains in health. Such choices are often difficult as the gains in one area can lead to a reduction in service or a limitation on the availability of resources elsewhere.

The Joint Venture has been working with those involved in these difficult choices in both health services and other organisations to help them improve:

- the nature of their collective investment in health;
- the extent to which health promotion and preventive services can be enhanced in commissioning for health gain;
- the capacity of those involved to use evidence from research and practice to guide their decisions and shape their priorities;
- the ability of staff to work in partnership beyond organisational and professional boundaries to achieve improved health for the greatest number.

The work continues as a three-year programme of local demonstration projects, with the twin aims of providing support to integrated commissioning, and identifying the critical success factors in meeting local and national health targets.

Robin Douglas
Office for Public Management

Jean Spray
Health Education Authority

Preface

This publication documents and reflects on a three-year programme of work begun in 1994 and completed in the summer of 1996 by the Health Education Authority (HEA) in association with the Office for Public Management (OPM).The stage was set in 1994 by a simulation event, 'Chameleon', which explored the challenges and opportunities for developing health promotion approaches within the emerging commissioning relationships in the NHS.

Here the learning from the original 'Chameleon' simulation event is summarised and four new projects – a research project exploring health promotion in primary care, a simulation event 'Roundabout', multi-agency action learning sets, and the health gain consultancy programme – are described. These projects, which are collectively referred to here as the Joint Venture, aimed to address those issues raised in 'Chameleon' by:

- improving the effectiveness and efficiency of the process of commissioning for health gain;

- supporting the development of health promotion in a primary care-led NHS;

- exploring ways of developing the capacity of health promotion specialists and others involved in the planning and delivery of health promotion interventions.

The Joint Venture was created to examine and influence changes in the ways that commissioning for improvements in health was evolving as a result of the rapid developments of health-care policies and systems in England between 1994 and 1996. A particular focus was on understanding how health promotion could be influential in delivering health gain within an emerging primary care-led NHS.

This report seeks to make a central contribution to the debate on how improved commissioning for health and health promotion might maximise their contribution to both population and individual health gain within a primary care-led NHS.

Chapter 1 outlines the policy context which informed the development of this work, and the history and development of the Joint Venture. Chapter 2 provides an overview of the Joint Venture, and a summary of the findings from the work of the projects, and Chapters 3, 4, 5 and 6 describe the design, implementation and outcomes of each of the projects in more detail.

1. The policy context

The new agenda in health care

International developments in health care[1] have demonstrated the widespread
centrality of the concept of health gain as a unifying concept for change within
health-care systems. This change requires health services to be commissioned
and provided in ways that maximise health outcomes from a health-care
budget that is limited or, in some cases, reduced. For most developed health-
care systems, such as those in the USA, Canada, UK, Scandinavia and the
Pacific region, there is some consensus that this might be best achieved within
a service framework focused towards, or led by, primary care.

The primary care-led NHS

In 1994 the Secretary of State for Health signalled a major expansion of the GP
fundholding scheme and indicated the government's intention to shift the NHS
towards primary care-led purchasing: 'The aim is for decisions about
purchasing and providing health care to be taken as close to the patient as
possible by GPs working closely with patients through primary health-care
teams'.[2] This was based on the belief that 'purchasing delivers more
appropriate services for patients when GPs are involved'.

Health authorities were to have a new role, they would:

● directly purchase for non-fundholding GPs and for specialist services;

● develop health strategies, and in so doing, involve local people, GPs and a
   number of relevant agencies;

● monitor the performance of GPs in the primary care-led purchasing system;

● support the development of the primary care-led purchasing system by
   offering advice, investment and training.

The partnership between GP fundholders and the health authority was seen as
critical to the success of the approach, especially where GPs needed to consider
health issues relating to populations and groups rather than individual patients.

In April 1995, the NHS Executive published the Accountability Framework[3]
within which it expects fundholders to operate. This framework presents GP
fundholders with four key accountabilities:

● Management accountability, statutorily, to the NHS Executive, to be
   managed through NHS Executive regional offices. Day-to-day

management responsibility will be with health authorities. Accountability will be exercised by fundholders through four main processes:

- publishing the annual practice plan;
- announcing major shifts in their purchasing intentions;
- reporting performance through annual reports to the health authority;
- holding performance review meetings with partners.

● Patient and community accountability, through:

- publishing information (e.g. annual practice plan, performance report);
- involving patients in service planning;
- ensuring effective complaints systems.

● Financial accountability, through:

- preparation of annual accounts for independent audit;
- providing information for monthly monitoring by the health authority;
- agreeing with the health authority how savings should be used;
- saying how local efficiency targets (set by the NHS Executive) will be met.

● Professional accountability, through:

- clinical audit of GMS activities;
- ensuring that agreed audit programmes are completed by hospital and community health-care providers.

The primary care-led NHS is based on these key policy drivers, and developments are taking place throughout the country. There are still, however, considerable uncertainties about its ultimate form – or forms. The extent to which fundholding or locality commissioning arrangements will be the dominant arrangements will depend on future government policies (including the recent White Paper[4] proposing alternative forms of GP contract), continuing GP interest, and developing capabilities. The degree to which health authorities will be the key co-ordinating body or replaced by other more localised arrangements is also unclear. And finally, the nature and extent of involvement of other organisations such as local authorities, commercial and voluntary organisations are continuing future challenges.

Health gain, effectiveness and efficiency

It is likely that the term 'health gain' was first used in the UK in a paper by the Welsh Health Planning Forum.[5] In 1990 the Welsh Office began to publish protocols[6] for investment in health gain focusing on health strategy, cost-effectiveness, evidence-based intervention, contracting, rationing/disinvestment and outcome assessment. In 1991 the World Health Organisation (WHO) Collaborative Centre for European Health Policy, proclaimed the 1990s the 'decade of health gain'. The first of the Health Gain Standing Conferences was called in Belfast in 1991. This was the result of a collaboration between East

Anglian Regional Health Authority, the Eastern Health and Social Services Board in Northern Ireland, and the Office for Public Management. From 1993 the newly formed Association of Public Health took over the organisation of this standing conference and a range of other activities to further the cause of outcome-based investment in health services, and to extend involvement in planning and policy development to a wide range of interests and professional groups.

In 1992 the national health strategy *The Health Of The Nation*[7] was published in England and the concept of health gain began to be widely used in relation to the national debate about improving health. However, the specific meaning or definition of health gain continues to be subject to much debate. Health gain can be defined as 'the cost effective, positive, planned and measurable health outcome arising from the application of health-care resources upon an individual or community or the social product of health arising from the impact of social systems on communities'.[8] Nonetheless Griffiths[9] suggests that although there seems to be a 'broad consensus over the value and location of the concept it is probably left broad because there is endless room for argument at the detailed level . . .'

The parameters of the health gain debate are usually taken to require a consideration of:

- efficiency
- effectiveness
- outcomes assessment
- evidence-based intervention and decision-making
- public participation and values
- health needs assessment
- variations or inequalities in health
- rationing and funding debates
- resource allocation
- development of measurement and procedural tools
- models of health and health development
- strategies for organisational change.

The Department of Health (DoH) has recently endorsed these priorities in England in its 1996/97 corporate contracting guidance to Health Authorities.[10] In this, the NHS Executive required commissioners to 'improve the cost effectiveness of services throughout the NHS, and thereby secure the greatest health gain from the resources available'.

The development of the Joint Venture

The new agenda in health, the move towards a primary care-led NHS and the focus on health gain require skills and approaches that are new to many managers and professionals in the NHS and beyond. In the field of improving population health, no one profession or sector controls all the levers necessary to bring about the changes required.

The Joint Venture described in this report was devised to address these issues. It was designed to create a flexible and interactive process through which key players from health and related organisations could develop solutions to the challenges posed by the new policy imperatives, and engage in personal and organisational learning.

In 1994, in response to the current DoH policy direction, the HEA commissioned OPM to develop a 'futures' simulation. This was named 'Chameleon',[11] reflecting the demands placed on health authorities in particular to develop the capacity to work equally well with providers, GPs, fundholders, the public and other organisations in their commissioning tasks – that is to modify their approach and style to influence and respond to the expectations of these diverse organisations. Chameleon explored issues of health promotion and commissioning for health gain within the newly emerging NHS structures.

The participants in Chameleon included GPs, health commissioners, and representatives of NHS trusts, the HEA, local authorities, voluntary and community groups, further and higher education, and the private sector. They were encouraged to use their experience and skill in communicating, lobbying and negotiating agreements. The time of the simulation was set at 'one year in the future' (that is, in 1996) and the policy context was restricted to just a few of the Health of the Nation target areas, namely sexual health, mental health, coronary heart disease (CHD), and black and minority ethnic health.

Through this exercise a number of issues emerged that highlighted difficulties limiting the capability of the various organisations represented to contribute effectively to improving the nation's health. Amongst these were:

- the difficulty of developing a workable and shared definition of 'health gain';

- the relative absence of effective levers to change 'traditional' patterns of health commissioning;

- the appreciation that it is not easy to integrate national policy imperatives (such as the Health of the Nation) with local agendas;

- the difficulty of making existing effectiveness and intervention data widely available and locally relevant to support evidence-based choices;

- the difficulty experienced by people and organisations outside the health service in influencing NHS structures and systems;

- the need to develop effective partnerships between individuals and organisations who together can make progress towards greater health gain.

Following Chameleon, further diagnostic work was undertaken by the HEA and OPM which involved interviews with chief executives of health authorities, GPs, health promotion specialists and others. As a result, four projects were

2. Summary of the learning

The design, implementation and outcomes of each of the Joint Venture projects are reported in detail in the following chapters. This chapter summarises the key themes and conclusions of the work and identifies considerations for the future.

The major themes which have emerged are:

● managing change effectively to achieve real gains in health;

● health gain – the usefulness or otherwise of this key concept in commissioning;

● evidence-based commissioning – the access to, and utilisation of research and practice-based evidence in commissioning and providing health-care services;

● a primary care-led NHS – from a policy directive through to practice experience and an effective reality;

● health promotion roles and tasks – an analysis of the current position and the future of health promotion specialists;

● health promotion and health gain in primary care – current practice and key levers for change;

● the contribution of health authorities, regional offices of the NHS Executive, local authorities and others to health gain;

● partnerships and inter-organisational activity – exploring the complexities and costs of developing and maintaining partnerships to plan and deliver services for health and social outcomes;

● devolution and fragmentation – consideration of the effects of devolution of key decision-making and rationing choices in the NHS, and the fragmentation and increased diversity of organisational arrangements at local levels.

Managing change effectively to achieve real gains in health

In all the projects much consideration focused around the key issue of managing change effectively. The discussions relating to leading and managing change produced useful reflections on the links between the 'big ideas', which can seem at times overwhelming or too diffuse to be manageable, and local practice. For example, one of the learning sets reflected that a direct focus on improving health through means that were simple, realistic and local – the 'Trojan mouse' approach – was both more manageable and more likely to bear fruit than other more global strategies.

Two elements were suggested by many participants as facilitatiing their own efforts to improve their effectiveness as change agents:

- The opportunity to synthesise their own knowledge and make it available to others through creating general models of commissioning for health gain which, they believed, represented an improvement on those in common use.

- Skills training to enhance capability in organisational change and development.

Increasingly it was recognised that it was not enough to be 'right' if you could not also persuade others to change or modify their behaviour. This capability to influence change is likely to be indicative of the extent of success or failure in any multi-agency, multi-professional context which is required to adapt in the direction of greater efficiency and effectiveness.

Since the Chameleon event took place in 1994 it appears that progress is being made in developing and understanding the potential of new levers to change patterns of health commissioning, and in enabling non-NHS agencies to influence the health agenda. In particular this is informed by a greater appreciation of the need for agencies and disciplines to work closely together – but not for everyone to do the same things – and an understanding of the relevance of the tools of change management and organisational development to make it happen. Given the progress that has been made there is a continuing need for support to help local actors bridge the gap between 'big ideas' and national policy drivers and their own endeavours which will make a difference to the health of local populations. In particular it is worth highlighting the need, which has clearly emerged from the projects, for some innovation in the processes by which current knowledge of good practice and effectiveness in relation to health promotion and health gain are synthesised and made available.

One particular point on managing the process of change towards health gain emerged from the Roundabout simulation. The method that was used involved trying to get agencies to collaborate in health gain activities by bidding for substantial project funding (10 per cent of the health authority's annual budget for each of three successive years). It was striking to see how difficult players found it to share their attentions effectively between designing innovative health gain initiatives, partnership-building, and positioning themselves to attract project funds. There was a genuine attempt to explore innovative health gain initiatives, but most of the energy and attention was absorbed by partnership-building and the bidding process. In the debriefing sessions, participants recognised this behaviour as genuine and one which reflected the actual experience in a specific initiative in the West Midlands.

When project funding is used as a device to pump-prime for change, there needs to be a powerful focus on the change objective or outcome to balance the pull towards attending merely to the bidding process. This focus on goals and balance are key tasks for all partners but an especially key task for (a) whoever has commissioned the project or their representatives, and (b) the project manager or project leader.

Overall, there was general agreement that one location of change management capability was clearly within the domain of health promotion. Health promotion specialists, supported by the HEA and programmes such as the health gain consultancy programme, were seen as unique and essential tools to meet the challenge.

Health gain – definitions and debates

In each project there were extensive discussions about the use and meaning of the idea of health gain. There was a search for clarity about which definitions were useful, and whose (patient, doctor, WHO, public health specialist, etc.) definitions should be most influential. Various definitions were considered, including the classic 'years to life, life to years', 'achieving an improvement in the health of a population', and 'mobilising positive influences of physical, social and environmental factors which can make major contributions to health improvement'.

The discussions led to a number of conclusions:

● Health gain still remains a useful concept, even though a number of commentators are critical of the lack of a single, widely recognised and accepted definition. Its prime use is in providing a strong, outcome-focused image to guide commissioning and service provision. It also encourages questions about how different choices or priorities can be compared by the extent to which they contribute to real gains in health for individuals or groups.

● There is a particular weakness in the concept when service responses require engagement from other organisations outside the direct health arena. Health gain has little currency in local authorities, for example. In these other agencies, alternative ways of describing outcomes need to be found. The projects often referred to 'health and social gain' as a means of overcoming these difficulties.

● The increasing emphasis on targeted investment to deal with inequalities in health and lifestyle choices, particularly those strategies focused on poverty and environmental issues, is creating some tensions in the use of the health gain concept. There are arguments that suggest that a purist approach, i.e. the greatest health gain for the greatest number from the least investment, may well undermine commitments to invest health resources in some of the poorest and most disadvantaged members of society. If it is argued that their propensity to gain from such investment is limited, then the resources made available to such groups may well become restricted. There may be a polarised, and potentially unhelpful debate emerging between health gain and targeted health investment.

There are some particular implications from the Joint Venture work for the development of a primary care-led NHS with a focus on health gain. It became evident through the work of the learning sets and the Roundabout simulation in particular, that no one is managing the whole process of health gain development, nor is any one agency or specialism able to cover all the ground by themselves. In the absence of any other co-ordinating mechanism, this may lead to possibly unsustainable pressure on health authorities (or health and local authority partnerships) as the only location where the various factors can come together. This observation deserves further attention. From a primary care perspective it was noted that there was a tendency to continually enlarge the definition of primary health care to include, for example, social services, housing and environment. This could be positive from a health gain point of view. However, there were also countervailing forces which are causing a growing reluctance of many GPs to take on anything which may be considered non-core activity. There is still scope to develop innovative ways of seeking to ensure that health and health-related services are relevant to patients and citizens while continuing to meet the wider health gain agenda without simply resorting to an assumption that GPs are the obvious and only proxy for the views of patients, or the central focus for population health improvement.

Since Chameleon, the introduction of the primary care-led NHS, Local Agenda 21, and the emphasis on evidence-based interventions among other policies, have to an extent shifted the focus of attention in the health gain debate. These new challenges both widen the field of relevant stakeholders and provide an antidote to any potential sense of complacency. The baseline of new skills and approaches needs to be shared, consolidated, and supported by accessible effectiveness data, none of which will be easily achieved. Nevertheless, as the participants in the Joint Venture found, the development of better commissioning for health gain is both an exciting and rewarding journey.

Evidence-based health promotion and the availability and acceptability of data

Participants in all the projects within the Joint Venture were interested in and very alert to the need to develop their knowledge about all forms of effective interventions, and of finding ways to create shifts towards these that are acceptable and provide value for money. To this end considerable emphasis was placed on sorting core data from research and evidence reviews, particularly within the learning sets. It is evident that there is still relatively little knowledge about the availability of health promotion effectiveness databases outside the health promotion field. This difficulty may be overcome by presenting this kind of effectiveness data in other formats and through different media – those that are commonly referenced by key professionals other than health promotion specialists. A secondary but equally important need is for guidance and support to local commissioners including GPs, as well as those outside the NHS, who are likely to welcome help in making sense of available evidence on health promotion effectiveness and good practice, and linking this to local circumstances. In areas where there are already good working relations between public health and health promotion specialists this task is becoming easier.

Using evidence was found to be problematic in other ways too. The experience was that in exploring the data, there was often much confusion and complexity in their interpretation. There were also a number of concerns, even where information about effectiveness was sound, about indications of difficulty in informing the key decision-makers and gaining the commitment of professionals to change their practices. A number of significant themes emerged, including the need:

● to extend the debate about evidence-based purchasing to a wider audience.

● at a local level, to set more appropriate criteria for the evaluation of health promotion interventions and the use of evidence in choosing programmes of work.

● for a careful assessment of what difference the availability of evidence will make in commissioning and service delivery decisions. It is currently somewhat fashionable to believe that much health investment will be modified once the evidence of effectiveness becomes available. However, it is more likely that changes will be made in a number of cases but in many others the evidence will be questioned, will be equivocal or will be contradicted by experience, vested interests or further research.

● to improve access to relevant evidence as the key to real influence in commissioning, particularly in a primary care-led NHS where GPs are influential in their initial assessment and co-ordinating roles. This will involve health promotion and public health specialists working closely together, providing advice and guidance to local service providers, particularly those in primary care settings. They will need to base this guidance on recognised 'best practice', which should be built on accessible evidence of effectiveness.

Some of this work may be appropriate for a special health authority like the HEA, other aspects might be more appropriate for the NHS Executive. Existing GPs are quite strongly influenced by their participation in postgraduate education forums. Other members of the primary health-care team are influenced by their own professional forums. It may be important to use these forums, and the 'gatekeepers' who control the agendas, as allies in managing change.

A primary care-led NHS

One of the most significant changes taking place in the NHS, particularly for those committed to extending the effectiveness of health promotion and education activities, is the shifting role and influence of primary care in commissioning decisions and in its extended involvement in providing co-ordination of the individual patient's experience in secondary care. The projects spent considerable time exploring the roles of health promotion in this changing environment and assessing the implications of further changes, including closer links with local authorities, greater investments in public and environmental health, extended use of outcome measures, and evidence-based health investment. The Roundabout simulation, in particular, exposed some of the many difficulties in developing the capacity of those in primary care to establish more strategic perspectives, understand the dynamics of partnership formation and joint working, and work with the broader systems of health and social care.

Defining the nature of 'a primary care-led NHS' was similar to the debates about health gain, and yielded similar results. The Department of Health guidance in EL (94)79 on the new role of the health authorities, and EL (95)54 setting the accountability framework for GPs, provides a clear focus for the development of primary care but still leaves much to be determined. The result of the work within the projects led to the following conclusions:

● GPs as central figures in the future of a primary care-led system will need considerable help in developing the potential in their roles to work more closely both with their local communities and individual patients in influencing service providers to be more responsive and sensitive to their needs. Their complex roles as commissioners, purchasers and providers will need careful attention, particularly in areas such as health promotion where there is limited experience of commitment to long-term investments in health, rather than providing responses to ill health.

● Information is crucial in enabling local decisions to be reached. This is still a significant gap as described by participants who are involved in locality and primary care-led commissioning arrangements. Greater coherence between public health and other commissioning activities, including health promotion, will be required to ensure that both local information, such as population and illness profiles, and activity data, such as patient flows and costs, is available to those involved in planning at the local level.

● The GP is not the only figure in a significant position in a primary care-led NHS, and fundholding is increasingly only a part of a complex range of organisational arrangements in primary care. There are other key members of the primary health-care team who are crucial to successful planning and action. The primary care service centres that are developing in many community settings can provide real opportunities for health promotion to develop long-term interventions.

Health promotion and health gain in primary care

Considerable valuable information was drawn from the interviews with the players within the primary health-care field about their existing health promotion and health gain work. The main findings are summarised here.

The range of current health promotion services is very varied. Much of this is because general practices are responding to local priorities – this responsiveness is precisely the characteristic which makes the primary care-led approach so attractive to policymakers. However, it is also clear that some of the variation is due to differing personal predilections, differing understanding about needs, an absence of shared protocols and standards, and a lack of consensus about the benefits of health promotion. This may well be leading to widely differing standards of preventive care. The research did not set out to define the extent of variation; however, according to the accounts of the GPs interviewed it clearly exists. This variation can be seen as a form of inequity. There are of course other forms of inequitable treatment in primary care which research is starting to reveal. Balarajan[12] for example, has shown that all minority ethnic groups experience longer waiting times in surgeries. The primary care-led system will need to recognise these variations as a risk factor for equity and establish the appropriate checks and controls.

GPs are key gatekeepers for and decision-makers about practice resources, policies and activities. However, other primary health-care team members are important too. Practice managers are able to significantly influence GPs. They provide links between GPs and the various professionals who come into contact with the practice, and co-ordinate and monitor practice activities and resources. Practice nurses not only have a lot of first-line contact with patients during health-promoting activities (and therefore are important sources of learning about patient needs) and maintain supplies of health promotion materials, but are key advisers and partners to GPs.

Health visitors emerge in this research as a particularly important group of people. They have a great deal of first-line contact with patients and others in their health-promoting activities. Their time is likely to constitute a major local investment in health promotion.

The future of health promotion in a primary care-led NHS is by no means guaranteed. This is not primarily because of overt opposition from GPs, although there is a small minority of doctors who either believe that health promotion is inappropriately sited in general practice or who do not believe that it has any benefit. But, as this research has shown, poor resourcing (money and information), or poorly targeted resourcing, the low level of skill development, insufficiently focused effort and weak accountability are key risk factors. The new environment is unlikely to have any immediate effect on the range of health promotion services which general practices offer. In time, however, if GPs have purchasing authority, they are likely to prefer health promotion programmes that are focused on specific morbidity and risk factors.

The research has made clear that GPs, acting on their own as single-handers or in groups, will find it difficult to purchase or commission services at a population level. A small minority will in any case reject this as an inappropriate role. The majority will agree to be involved in some way in purchasing or commissioning processes, but their natural focus is at the level of the individual patient. They feel uncomfortable with the population focus, have difficulty developing a strategic capability and feel that they lack the necessary skills. To meet this challenge successfully, GPs and their primary health-care teams will need considerable support, especially from the health authority, but perhaps also from national agencies. The support must deliver two types of resourcing – information and skills development.

General practices will need help in understanding the health needs of their practice populations. For health promotion, this will mean the provision of information about demography, epidemiology and social factors. In practice, to provide this information could involve mapping known morbidity and risks on to local population sub-sets, thus creating 'local' population profiles. It may also mean undertaking focused local studies, and developing and linking practice information systems with those of other practices (admitting that there could be difficulties here relating to confidentiality and territorialism), and with health authority systems – this is already happening in a number of areas.

The health authority–GP relationship will assume greater significance in the future, and will constitute a critical factor for the success of the new system. The relationship between GPs and the public health function will be particularly important. There are likely to be consequent internal changes which need to be considered within the health authority in order to facilitate this relationship. One of these is that public health specialists will need consultancy skills; it is probable that this will be required in relation not only to the gathering and dissemination of information and the development of effective practice, but also in relation to organisation development. If this is too much to expect from public health alone, then other agencies, particularly health promotion, will need to be brought into the relationship set.

Information will be a key resource in the primary care-led system, and how information is gathered and linked is especially important. The health authority is in a relatively good position to connect information from diverse sources. The issue of linking is important, e.g. ethnic group data from hospital in-patients (collected from April 1995) can be most effectively used only when linked to other information which will reveal patterns in access to health services and in morbidity.

For GPs, and possibly for practice managers, a key requirement will be the development of strategic capability – being able to understand and use external data, to conceive and plan over longer-term timescales, to adapt and direct resources, organisation structures and people to strategic purposes and to develop the inter-agency partnerships which are so crucial for the achievement of health outcomes.

Finally, if GPs are to develop in this way, it must be considered what the resultant effect is of GPs spending less time in patient consultation. This is an important issue, because it affects the basic dynamics of the primary health-care system.

The work of the projects strongly suggests the following development areas need to be addressed to assist GPs in becoming more centrally involved in the health gain agenda:

● Develop a better understanding of the different interpretations of the primary care-led system. It is important to explore areas both where the direction is clear and where it is less certain. The discussion needs to focus especially on how to strengthen accountability of GPs for non-GMS performance, including the Health of the Nation and other national targets and priorities.

● Build the relationship between GPs and the health promotion, informatics and public health functions in health authorities. This is key to helping GPs move successfully between the individual patient and the population level, and to enable them to develop strategic perspectives. Doing this successfully is likely to mean answering three questions about organisational issues within the health authority:

(i) Does the relationship between the informatics and public health functions facilitate an effective flow of information between GPs and the health authority? The flow needs to be two way, encouraging GPs to collect and share practice-based data and giving GPs demographic and epidemiological information. Much already takes place through the Public Health Annual Report, but an approach more focused on the specific needs of general practice may be required.

(ii) Does the public health function have sufficient resources to carry out this work? A primary care-led system will lead to a multiplicity of primary care players entering the commissioning arena. If this entry is to mean more than simply additional transactional costs, then some investment may need to be made in servicing and supporting their information needs.

(iii) Does the public health function have the right capability to perform this new function effectively? Public health specialists may need to develop consultancy skills in order to develop their relationship with GPs. At the very least, their relationship with others, including health promotion specialists, in the health authority, and regional office personnel responsible for organisation development will need to be strengthened.

● Facilitate the development of networking and partnerships with other stakeholders. There are potentially very many individuals and groups with an interest here, and it would be wise to begin by focusing on the few but key players, one of which should be the local authority.

● Carry out development work on individual roles and skills in primary health-care teams, in particular with practice nurses, practice managers and GPs.

Health promotion specialists and the roles and tasks of health promotion

A series of strong messages has emerged for specialists in health promotion roles. In summary, these messages include:

● A realisation that the changes currently taking place in the NHS in particular, but also across the public services, are forcing a major reappraisal of the possibilities and future of health promotion services. This is not entirely a recent phenomenon, but the pace and extent of changes in commissioning and in primary care are bringing a set of pressures that are of a new order.

● The opportunities to explore the idea of a health gain consultancy role provided a realistic platform from which to rehearse a number of these possible new ways of working. However, the notion of the health gain consultant is only one of a number of options that health promotion specialists should explore, as it emphasises a move towards a more generic role and probably a much closer integration with public health. There are other models that signal greater independence from both purchasers and providers. Such agency arrangements may take health promotion beyond the NHS, if broader-based responses to health gain include local authorities, voluntary bodies and independent organisations.

● Alongside a wider and more public assessment of the range of options for future roles and tasks of health promotion specialists, should go an appraisal of the different contributions that may be made in the system of planning and delivering services for health gain. There have been a number of studies considering where health promotion should be located in a changing NHS, but these are ultimately sterile if they do not identify what health promotion can do (and is currently doing) in these different settings. It is unhelpful to debate constantly whether health promotion should be located in the purchasing function or on the provider side, or even whether it should become an independent or freestanding agency. Experience from those involved in the Joint Venture indicates that this is much less important than clarifying the potential roles and tasks that require their specific competencies. The three-part description used in the Joint Venture to explore the changing nature of health promotion has the following components:
  ○ message development;
  ○ message delivery;
  ○ development of the capacity to both develop and deliver health promotion messages.

● It was clear that as the demands on health promotion specialists change, then new skills will be needed to meet these challenges. Within both the action learning sets and the health gain consultancy there were indicators of these needs for change. The basic skills that many health promotion specialists have developed are well attuned to such demands. Such people are often experienced in inter-organisational working, they regularly have to work through influence rather than positional authority, many are experienced in community development approaches and recognise the requirements of systemic approaches to change.

It was also clear, however, that considerable work will be necessary to provide a 'shape' to these competencies in ways that allow them to be explicitly developed and used in new ways. For example, there was often a reluctance to become visible when using individual and collective influence, ideas of 'managing up' were somewhat alien, and taking leadership roles in local commissioning activities was seen as very difficult. Such difficulties will need to be overcome if there is to be real influence from this group of people in the future. Skills in working on strategy and organisational change will also need to be developed if the professional expertise of this group is to be heard.

● The previous point focused on capability development and change. This point is an extension of this idea, in that it relates directly to extending power and influence. Two main elements appear to hold back health promotion in this area:

  ○ The language and focus of much health promotion activity is distant from many of the key players in health. It must be placed on their agenda, but in terms which key players understand.

  ○ Health promotion specialists must learn to recognise the political nature of organisations and the way that decisions are made. For many there is still an expectation that logical argument or a 'real understanding' of the problem will lead ultimately to the correct answer. Nothing could be further from the truth. Influence will be gained by understanding these realities and making judgements about how best to work within such a system to achieve real health gain.

● Networking is extensive in this field. There are some dangers in the existing arrangements in that they still tend to focus on specific geographical patches or around professional or issue-based interest groups. Careful thinking should be undertaken about how best to develop such networks in the light of the changes described above. There is a real danger of the existing networks being distracted by old issues as the new demands are made, and new possibilities are available to be exploited.

An assumption underlying the Joint Venture was that the roles of those involved directly in health promotion and in health promotion services will have to be reshaped to meet the requirements of a changing NHS. This was confirmed during the projects by almost all participants, with health promotion specialists recognising the need for more strategic influence in commissioning and an extension of their facilitative roles with local providers, particularly GPs.

Those from non-health promotion backgrounds were also clear about the need for change. They expressed a desire for better advice on the potential for effectiveness in any health promotion activity and greater freedom to develop their own local strategies to meet the needs of their local population or patients. The Joint Venture triggered a number of possibilities. For example, in the action learning sets, many examples emerged of collaboration arrangements between health promotion and public health or primary care providers to develop strategies to meet specific health gain targets. The health gain consultancy programme explored the hypothesis that the emerging role of the health promotion specialist was in influencing commissioning and service provision decisions through the use of relationships and expertise, rather than either the use of line authority or by direct service activity. The participants recognised the considerable possibilities inherent in such an approach and have continued enthusiastically to develop these ideas.

In the achievement of health gain there is also a recognition that the roles of health promotion will extend beyond the confines of the NHS. For example, a number of participants recognised opportunities for involvement with local authorities, voluntary agencies and commercial organisations in local regeneration activity, joint bids for resources and the achievement of health and social benefits through investment in infrastructure development. This is an area in which only a limited number of participants in the projects had any experience.

The Joint Venture has highlighted the need for health promotion professionals to define more clearly what it is that they do, and to find ways of engaging others in this process. The definition of what might be the basis of health gain consultancy is a negotiated one. That is, it needs to be given definition by purchasers, providers and service users as well as by the profession itself.

The contributions of health authorities, regional offices and the NHS Executive, local authorities and others to health gain

In both Chameleon and Roundabout, the health authorities and the regional office came in for some criticism. To some extent this was predictable as they are significant points of strategic influence and are expected to use their influence rather than attempt to direct patterns of service activity. They also have to do this in a very limited time frame with many conflicting demands upon them. Specific learning for these organisations from the Roundabout simulations includes:

- achieving an effective balance between an open facilitative style and the ability to offer clear leadership when required is the most difficult dilemma that must be managed by regional, national and health authority staff. A more open recognition of this dilemma would facilitate the involvement of others and potentially reduce some of the existing tensions.

- a preoccupation with contracting often obscures attention to the real health gain issues. This was reinforced in respect of the time taken in dealing with acute sector issues and the limited attention given to health promotion, which not only takes up a tiny proportion of the direct expenditure, but is often a very small item on these organisations' agendas. More clarity about where the values of public health and health gain fit into the daily practice of the work of health authorities and regional offices could lead to some interesting reappraisals of priorities.

- partnership working is crucial to these agencies in meeting their goals. The skills in this area are seen to vary widely from one agency to another. More coherence about what is required at both the individual and organisation level will be needed if partnerships inside the NHS – with GPs and other primary care staff – and outside the health service – with social services, housing, the police, voluntary bodies, etc. – are to be nurtured, developed and maintained.

● greater understanding of the extent of the changes that have been introduced at local level, such as GP involvement in commissioning, locality purchasing and other service planning arrangements and their effects, is essential if working relationships are to be enhanced.

● health authorities need to be clearer and more explicit about how they plan to implement their three key roles – strategy, monitoring and support. With this more open approach should come clear indicators of how they aim to develop local capabilities to deliver on both national and local health gain targets.

● leadership in commissioning will rest with the health authorities through their relationships with primary care purchasers and locality commissioning arrangements. Explicit commitment to the use of evidence in decisions and systemic, outcome-oriented approaches to contracting will lead towards a greater likelihood of achieving health gain.

● regional offices will need to explore the tensions between their new civil service, 'light-touch' roles and the need for involvement in local issues and strategic concerns that are wider than the individual authority. There are a number of areas where a co-ordinating or supporting capability would be very useful. For example, in terms of primary care development, a regional response on some issues could be much more effective and efficient than many local initiatives. In addition, work to assess the usefulness of effectiveness data or the provision of commissioning guidance could form part of the regional role.

Local authorities can add value to the health gain work of health agencies through:

● bringing practical experience and understanding of the broader social determinants of health;

● their generally greater experience of community development;

● their networks of contacts with community organisations;

● their potentially powerful role as advocates of community involvement and informal community accountability;

● their statutory involvement in community care planning;

● their statutory responsibility for economic development and their involvement in urban regeneration.

Senior local authority managers are experienced negotiators and are comfortable and well equipped to take part in strategic partnerships. The downside here is that their firm assertion of legitimacy based on formal local accountability and their strong base in communities, alongside their size and status, gives them a weight within partnerships which can over-determine the interests of other players.

Many of the points made in respect of managers within the NHS apply to others in local authorities, voluntary or independent organisations and other agencies involved in the achievement of health gain. Additionally, they should consider:

● the extent to which, in their involvement with health-led initiatives, they are moving away from the priorities and strategies of their own organisations. If there is a degree of consistency and shared benefits from the work, then there will be few problems. However, where the health gain priorities diverge, such managers and professionals will face personal dilemmas about how to manage the gaps. This should be recognised within the NHS, and support given where necessary. Alternatively health objectives may need to be modified to accept the need for mutual organisational and community benefit.

● joint development opportunities are often helpful in reducing these tensions and providing the means to address stereotyped assumptions and behaviour patterns, in addition to developing joint strategies to address tensions between partnership bodies. The Joint Venture was considered to have initiated such possibilities, particularly in the action learning sets.

Partnerships – multi-agency learning and working

In all projects the task of developing effective multi-agency learning and working to deliver health gain was acknowledged as challenging.

The progress of the action learning sets, both in content and process, substantially illustrated the nature of multi-agency learning and working. Starting from a felt need to define the territory, the action learning sets worked towards the adoption of 'good enough' definitions of health gain and/or health improvement. In this the more important aspects were active listening and open consideration of others' viewpoints, rather than achieving unchallengeable correctness. The concept of a 'working definition' is particularly apt here, since the main outcome from these discussions was a shared understanding of the scope and direction of the work and each other's relation to it, sufficient to allow participants to move on to the next stage.

From here participants shared their own local experiences of seeking to achieve improvements in health. There is no doubt that these exchanges were of considerable value, creating a shared ethos of co-operative enquiry, and providing some immediately relevant ideas which could be tried out locally. This also helped to establish a deeper sense of different agencies' concerns, constraints and aspirations, which was fundamental to developing the ability to move forward together, rather than as separate and distinct individuals. It is interesting to note how many participants referred to the building of trust through this process as an important underpinning to the work that followed. On reflection, many commented that this might be difficult to recreate in a local setting. This difficulty presents something of a dilemma for further field development, but is perhaps best taken as an indication of the amount of work necessary to create the local conditions through which health improvement can be addressed. Local alliances must develop a clear sense of scope and direction; because they require a lot of effort they should not be assumed to be a good thing in themselves without further consideration of the intended outcomes. However, there is clear evidence that much, if not most, of the health gain agenda can only be achieved through focused partnerships.

Partnership-building emerged as a major theme in the Roundabout simulation as well as the learning sets. Judging by participant feedback, it became a major source of interest and learning. Players found the process of developing partnerships both challenging and interesting, and valued the different perspectives which partnership brought, through broadening traditional notions of health and linking health and social dimensions. But partnership building also proved to be tremendously energy absorbing and involved considerable transactional costs. At times in the simulation it seemed as if partnership-building became the end rather than the means. None the less, effective partnerships between agencies is likely to be a key variable in any health gain project. As such, partnership (or intersectorality, as it is sometimes known) does constitute a primary objective of the health gain approach.

The Roundabout simulation showed that effective partnership-building requires a framework. This framework needs to accomplish three agreements:

● how money and other resources can be pooled or jointly spent;

● the purpose and outcome for which the partnership is being established and the method by which accountability is to be exercised;

● developing legitimacy for the partnership project at the top and within the partner organisations.

Such a framework needs negotiation with other partners. But this does not mean that health service organisations should not be clear about the principles of the framework when they are about to enter partnerships.

In addition to these experiences, a number of related themes emerged for future consideration in the area of joint working. There was a clear recognition that health gain only provided an *introduction* to the possibilities for collaboration and that a wider definition will be required to gain full commitment from local authorities, voluntary organisations, and so forth. In particular:

- the complexity and obscurity of professional language, particularly in health, needs careful attention in order to enable partnerships to be established with clear understanding, and maintained, particularly when under stress;

- issues of trust were seen as central to effective partnerships and took some time and attention to establish;

- the HEA's work on healthy alliances provided a reference point in these discussions and many considered that it could be extended to assess the costs and gains from building such alliances.

Devolution and fragmentation – managing change in an increasingly complex and confusing environment

There is little doubt that the devolution of decision-making to primary care on many issues has potential benefits in developing a community-based service, responsive to patients and citizens. However, as the recent Audit Commission report on fundholding[13] demonstrates, there are costs in terms of variability of service and lack of coherence and control. The focus for many discussions in the projects was how to achieve the benefits of more localised decision-making without the danger of increasing inequalities in services.

The health authority role in providing links between population-based choices and local interests, represented often by GPs, was considered crucial in attempting to achieve the benefits from devolved systems. The health promotion role in such processes is very important in facilitating discussions and decisions at both the strategic and the local levels. There is also a danger in situations of increasing complexity to look for simple role models or 'recipes', particularly in terms of organisational arrangements and structures. The participants recognised that differences were to be welcomed, as long as there was some evaluation of the effectiveness of outcomes of their work and there was an opportunity for learning to be available to others.

The Joint Venture activities provided a focal point for people with a commitment to health promotion to explore shared concerns, practice experience and assess the potential of strategies for change. As the fragmentation within the NHS increases, it is easy for health promotion to be moved between purchasers and providers with no clear definition of ownership or responsibility. The projects gave people the opportunity to consider the consequences of this and at the same time to look for ways of ensuring the centrality of health promotion to health gain.

3. The Roundabout Simulation

Design

Roundabout was designed as an open behavioural simulation to explore how health gain might fare in a primary care-led NHS. While it brought together around 30 policymakers, managers, GPs and other clinicians from the West Midlands, the event was designed to be of relevance to other urban areas.

The issues explored were:

- If it is true that GPs are generally focused on the health-care needs of individual patients, how can attention be focused on the needs of people at a group or population level (especially in relation to variations in health)?
  ○ What are the implications for data gathering?
  ○ Will the roles and relationships within the practice change?

- What factors support the relationship between GPs and health authorities? How can these be facilitated? What are the problems, if any, of one partner focusing on population needs and the other focusing, primarily, on individual patient needs?

- Are there any tensions to be managed in being both provider and purchaser of health services?

- What are the issues in GPs working for health gain, not only for health care?
  ○ What information is required and how will it be accessed?
  ○ What multi-agency relationships and partnerships need to be established?
  ○ Can time be found and used for this purpose?
  ○ What products and services will be required?

- Will primary health-care team members play a bigger part than GPs in health gain (and within this, health promotion)?

- Will GPs and primary health-care teams need to develop their skills further if they are to deliver local versions of the Health of the Nation targets effectively?

- Should health promotion budgets be held separately or should they be integrated into general purchasing budgets?

- How can, or should, health authorities' contributions to tackling the issues outlined above be developed?

- How will health authorities hold GPs to account for performance on health promotion goals?

- Population boundaries will not fall neatly into general practice areas – how will, or should, health authorities, GPs and others work in collaboration across practices?

- Working for health gain will involve linking with communities and community organisations, other statutory organisations, voluntary organisations, and even with the private sector. What are the obstacles and opportunities facing the key players in working in this way?

- How will the dynamics of the health-care system change?

- Will the configuration of key players change?

Open simulations take as their starting point the assumption that everything is open to negotiation. When applied to an examination of large, complex systems – like the NHS – it is assumed that what happens will be determined to a considerable extent by the interaction between the players, as national, organisational and/or professional interests are pursued.

The intention of the Roundabout simulation was to model the diversity and apparent randomness of organisation-wide changes. It allowed for the continual renegotiation of rules, conventions and structures as an essential part of the process of the event. Indeed, the lessons learned from these interactions were amongst the most profound to emerge from the simulation.

One important aspect of open simulations is that participants are not expected to 'role-play' as a means of simulating reality. Rather, players are allocated positions with which they are already familiar in 'real life', e.g. the role of 'chief executive' is taken on by a real chief executive; actual practice managers take on the part of practice managers, and so on. To simulate the context in which play is to take place, participants are provided with a pack of data about a fictional 'patch'. The information is based on real data from actual localities, and is designed to be realistic.

Although it was theoretically possible to play out the full complexity of commissioning and providing primary care services in an urban setting, the practical issues of designing and staging an event on that scale led the simulation designers to create a stylised 'slice' of the broad range of services. In doing so, the aim was to simplify the real world sufficiently to provide insights at a general level, whilst ensuring that sufficient realism was retained to make it a world to which the players could relate.

This shift from reality to realism involved reducing the number of services and providers, simplifying the activity and financial information (yet retaining its 'authenticity'), and accelerating the rate at which time passed. This symbolic version of the real world was designed to allow the fundamental dynamics of the health system to emerge quickly and clearly during each round of the simulation. Participants were free to talk to whomever they wished, to come to understandings they felt were necessary, striking whatever deals they thought were appropriate. Players were encouraged to act as they normally would under the usual 'rules of engagement' of the NHS.

The General Election took place six months before Roundabout began. The result was a minority Labour government. To date, the Secretary of State for Health had not made any major pronouncement on the NHS. Therefore there had been no significant change in health policy, nor any large-scale surge in funding. Labour remained committed to replacing the purchaser–provider split with a planner–provider split, leaving intact the fundamental dynamics of what had hitherto been referred to as the 'internal market'.

It was clear that the new government was keen to support the shift to a primary care-led system. It wanted GPs to be closely involved in the definition of service need and in planning for services, primarily through locality planning forums. The health authority was seen by the new government as being a key player, bringing primary care agencies into the planning process. However, it seemed unlikely that the government would want to encourage funds to be placed in the hands of primary care agencies, and health authorities were likely to be the favoured locus for funding. Ministers were said to be unhappy with the accountability of fundholding GPs, and a task force was appointed two months after the election to look at better accountability and to advise the government on this.

Players were reminded of Labour's manifesto declaration of a strong commitment to reduce health inequalities. A task force had been set up to advise the Secretary of State on a strategy to reduce health inequalities in the British population. Health promotion was likely to be an important area.

Although the post-election situation was characterised by considerable uncertainty there were some quite strong signals about the direction of change. Some of the changes were important, but they seemed unlikely to alter the fundamental dynamics of the health-care system. Heat was certainly being generated in discussions of the options.

Roundabout took place in a fictional environment – Trumpton. Trumpton was modelled on an actual municipality in the Black Country, from which real data were borrowed, anonymised and re-shaped. The players were given data which included social, economic, demographic and epidemiological dimensions.

Players were presented with the scenario that the new government had decided to commission pilot studies in four 'typical' areas across the country in order to develop their longer-term policy. The purpose of the pilots was to see how best the experience of the NHS in achieving health gain – through, for example, such initiatives as healthy alliances, health promotion, disease prevention, clinical effectiveness – could be used to reduce health inequalities.

Each pilot health authority was expected to work with its health partners over the coming year to produce a 'development plan' for approval by the NHS Executive. Innovation was encouraged. Through this plan the health authority was able to bid for up to 10 per cent of the current health authority budget for three years as pump-priming money. After that the authority would revert to standard population-based resource allocation and any proposed permanent changes would have to be self-financing.

The NHS Executive let it be known that they could be persuaded about almost anything as long as:

- it did not commit them to a growth in overall expenditure in subsequent years;

- there was genuine local support for the developments – especially from GPs, the consultants and the local authority;

- there was good evidence for a case that the changes would reduce health inequalities.

The NHS Executive also said that, to be successful, bids must pay sufficient attention to planning and strategy development and to any new information needs. Any required changes in managerial and accountability relationships would have to be explicit.

The simulation began with a start-up conference, the Consensus Conference, organised by the health authority which aimed to establish a partnership of key players who would bid to become one of the four pilot projects. The Consensus Conference was followed by a series of individual and group negotiations and relationship development, punctuated by meetings of the steering group established at the end of the conference. Pressure – and a sense of drama – was exerted on the players by requiring them to appear in a radio programme at the end of Day 1, and having to present their bid to the regional office team at the end of play on Day 2. The event ended with written evaluation and individual and group de-briefing sessions – this was particularly important in helping participants become aware of what they had learned, and capturing this in a form which could be used for analysis and future development.

Outcomes

The following outcomes were identified by the participants:

The health authority was keen to facilitate a consensus between the various agencies involved by endeavouring to 'play a lead role but without forcing its own agenda on to others'. It was concerned that health and health gain (rather than vested interests) should remain the focus of all the discussions and agreements made. The authority aimed to build effective alliances with other key players (particularly the local authority) and, therefore, saw it as crucial to gain clarity as to what each agency was able to offer. Overall, the authority sought to ensure that, within the bounds of the simulation, projects with clear outcomes and delivery should emerge as the basis for the bid for additional funding.

Despite intentions to the contrary, the health authority found it increasingly difficult to broker an integrated bid. With money at stake, and without a 'common language', the very real differences in values, service aspirations and desires to influence the final bid, between some (though not all) of the key players, became evident. The authority concluded that it was not able to provide an effective lead founded upon an evidence-based public health perspective. Gradually the basis for the bid had moved away from a focus on reducing health inequalities towards the development of health service infrastructures. However, the emphasis on effective community development was maintained. As a consequence the final presentation represented the 'inevitable compromises necessary to reach a win–win' and saw the key players bidding for resources to fund a somewhat disparate group of projects.

There were many factors that contributed to the shift towards infrastructures, some of which were outside the influence of the health authority. The health authority believed that the alliances struck between the various agencies involved, and especially its own with the local authority, constituted a particularly positive outcome. Indeed throughout the simulation, the health authority and the local authority used their combined influence to press for a broader perspective on health, which the health authority felt it achieved. Conversely, the health authority believed that its alliance with the local authority weakened its ability to give the lead that appeared to be required by the health service stakeholders. The health authority felt that some of the more dominant health service providers remained too preoccupied with health services.

With hindsight, the health authority decided that it should have done more to ensure that all the players fully understood the bidding criteria. The authority would have liked to have considered earlier elements of the strategy, other than those promoted by GPs. Building in more consultation (especially with the community) from the start would have helped. The health authority recognised its pivotal role and (second time around) it would have produced a clearer public health analysis that would have identified achievable targets.

The health authority players concluded that the development of a shared language and understanding between the agencies involved was vital to the process of creating inter-organisational strategies to achieve health gain. They also said they experienced the power of different agencies, GPs especially, to block innovative strategies, albeit unwittingly. The health authority was impressed by the scope of the role and experience of the local authority and this served to emphasise the importance of local councils in achieving health gain.

The regional office of the NHS Executive was keen to ensure that the guidelines on how the pump-priming money should be spent were closely followed. Clear and realistic objectives, founded on evidence-based, clinically effective practices, were vital. It stressed the value and importance of multi-agency partnerships and it was very keen for the principles and practices of project management to be woven into all the ideas for various initiatives. The regional office was clear about the necessity of avoiding any revenue implications beyond the three years that could not subsequently be afforded. It aimed to maintain 'political cover' and it wanted 'to keep the trusts in line' (*sic*) with all the parameters laid down.

At the end of the simulation, the regional office was disappointed that the final bid was not a coherent project plan. It felt that the health authority had not responded adequately to its briefs from the region. While it recognised there had been difficulties in getting financial data it was somewhat unsettled that the long-term revenue implications had not been adequately addressed.

The region declared in the early Consensus Conference that it wished to see issues addressed that were pertinent to the needs of the people of Trumpton. Once the conference closed, the region concluded that there were the beginnings of some significant conflicting ambitions between the trusts and that the 'hard message of sustainability after three years' had yet to sink in. However, as the region did not want to cut across the health authority, it felt unable to get directly involved in trying to sort out these difficulties. Instead it chose to continue pressing the health authority on the funding criteria.

After the final bid presentation, the region asked some very pointed questions of the health authority regarding project management and whether the authority had any evidence that lifestyle changes would actually bring any benefit to health gain or tackling health inequalities. The region was later to conclude that the proposal had very little vision of health gain.

On reflection, the region said that it would have worked more closely with the local authority to generate more base data on health inequalities and status whilst encouraging the local authority in its bid for improving health gain. The regional executive might have begun discussions with the local authority sooner to explore the possibilities for joint employment contracts and other mechanisms to bind the various agencies together. It would have stressed more – perhaps by making it a criterion – the need for any proposals to be primary care-led.

The region was somewhat surprised by the compliant role played by the various GP groups during the simulation and said that, based on real life, it would have expected a lot more lobbying from them.

The local authority consisted of both officers and councillors who worked together as a team throughout the simulation. The council's aims were to ensure that it had a leading role in the discussions and in the final proposal, and that its corporate concern for equality and community development would figure greatly. They were keen to build partnerships with all the other players, and in particular to push for ever more involvement and influence from the players representing the community and for a wide concept of health.

Overall, the council felt that it had been reasonably successful since it had met with 'less than the normal resistance' to involving community bodies and as a consequence had managed to maintain and integrate its political philosophy within the final proposal. The council considered that it had managed to shape, lead and co-ordinate the work leading up to the final bid. It was also happy that it did not take on what it perceived to be health issues and stayed close to its local authority role.

The council began with some caution about the role of the region, seeing it as somewhat distant. But it was keen to offer help based upon its experience of working with Single Regeneration Budget (SRB) bids. Interestingly, it was later to reflect surprise at the lack of knowledge of its role amongst many of the health service participants.

Chairing the steering group that met to pull together the final proposal allowed the council to impress upon its health colleagues the importance of linking in with council services such as housing and existing community development initiatives.

On reflection, the council said it would aim to network even more with other groups and try to understand their various interests better. It concluded that 'influence and negotiation are the name of the game'. It would have liked to talk more with the GPs about consultation. It might have done more to encourage Private Finance Initiative (PFI) funding and it would have liked to make sure that the regional office was supporting government policy.

Overall, the council believed that it remained too easy to pay only lip service to community participation. It was concerned about the sheer complexity of managing the funding of continuing resources and would have liked more time to consider how best to manage the inputs from the private and voluntary sectors. The council was left wanting a far clearer definition of primary care-led purchasing, and looked to the lead agency to set more helpful guidelines.

Primary care was represented by three groups: a total purchaser, a fundholding practice, and a non-fundholding practice. At the beginning these three groups worked independently but as the simulation proceeded they worked more and more together.

Initially the total purchaser wanted to ensure that in addressing health inequalities the health provision for their patients would be protected and indeed developed. They were concerned that tackling health inequalities might mean compromising with the lowest common denominator. They were also keen to minimise any extra work falling on GPs.

The fundholding practice wanted to ensure that their services were improved and not capped. They wanted the final proposal to focus on tackling health inequalities there through improving access for people from minority ethnic groups, and developing their existing health promotion activity of CHD risk management. At an individual level, members of this group were keen to test their influence and to explore how far their own perceptions were mirrored by their team members.

The non-fundholding practice wished to promote the services they already offered and identify ways of improving and supporting them to the benefit of their practice population. They were keen to develop those services in particular where they had evidence to suggest that they could be very effective (e.g. in the treatment of depression, CHD prevention and diabetic care). They too wished to avoid any erosion of existing services.

Given the close correspondence between the aims of the three groups it was not surprising that they came together before the end of the simulation and later reviewed their collective successes and disappointments together. Overall, the GPs were content that there was no erosion of the services that they offer. Moreover they felt there was not even an attempt to damage their services. All the groups commented that they had formed successful alliances with many of the other players and they valued working with these partnerships.

At the conference, the total purchaser, asserting its own position as one of the larger purchasers, expressed support for the bid and was eager to have a major role as a joint purchaser with the health authority. It did express concern about the possibilities for increased workload arising from the funds. Members were also somewhat cautious about sharing data, particularly with the private organisation 'Lifestyle'.

By the second day the GPs had formed an alliance, and used their strength in numbers to negotiate with the acute trust, the community trust, the council and others. Indeed the acute trust suggested that they join forces because the GPs are 'more of a single mind than they realise. It would be very useful to have a coherent view from the GPs'. Behind this statement perhaps, was the desire by some of the players for the GPs to develop a more strategic perspective that also took into account the wider health-care system outside their own practices and patients.

The GPs made it clear to the community health trust that they did not want to see a trust merger, believing that this would not benefit the local communities. Instead the GPs and the community trust developed the idea of a 'hub and spoke service', offering facilities to provide information and support for the community, particularly in relation to mental health. Very quickly the council's support was sought and obtained.

On reflection the GPs emphasised the importance of a common language to underpin any developments. Such a language must not only bridge the gap between GPs and other agencies, especially the local authority, but also with their own patients. They recognised the value and importance of networking, time-consuming though it may be, in achieving this common language and the resulting productive partnerships. They all stressed the importance of having good information about the health status of the various groups so that an essential assessment of needs could be carried out, and raised the possibility of finding ways to 'share' resources with the local authority. One practice left with the desire to explore more options concerning the involvement of the voluntary sector and the community at large in developing services.

During the simulation, GPs were struck by the importance of information (epidemiological and socio-demographic) in developing a broadly-defined evidence-based approach to health gain. Equally, they began to see the relationship with the local authority, which included the social services, economic development and environmental departments, as very important and were interested in findings ways of developing this relationship.

The GP groups, both fundholding and non-fundholding, worked throughout with a narrow focus and an essentially defensive position. It was striking to see the paradox of financially powerful GP groups exerting only limited influence within the health-care system. It seems that without a strategic capability and access to appropriate information, financially powerful primary care players will be unable to change the fundamental dynamics of the health-care system in a coherent way for desirable health outcomes. Overall they experienced considerable difficulty in:

● developing a strategic perspective;

● understanding and using all of the pressure points in the health-care system and in the broader system of health and social care;

● setting partnership relationships and exploring networks of relationships beyond the immediate ambit of current operations.

The community trust included the health promotion unit, and naturally one of its aims was to ensure that health promotion (rather than simply disease prevention) was represented in the bid. It also wanted to ensure that the wider determinants of health were addressed, particularly through empowering the local community to determine health and social care outcomes. It was keen to establish links with other agencies and offer support.

At the end of the simulation, the trust was satisfied that health promotion was integral to the bid, seeing it as part of the community development component where the wider determinants of health were also recognised. That said, the trust, like many others, expressed concern that the professionals remained too much at the centre and, as such, the overall approach adopted was not empowering.

The community trust tackled the issues in hand on two fronts. In the Consensus Conference it not only emphasised the objectives described above but also, and early on, began talking about its estate problems. After the conference it quickly canvassed support from the GP total purchasers for allocating some of their resources to improving its mental health resources. The trust also sought support from the health authority for improvements to its information systems.

On reflection, the trust was unhappy that the steering group did not capture all the good ideas that were floated, and recognised that it would need far more definite plans to take to the community. It felt it would need to get more involved with the community and local pressure groups far sooner and use the media more to broadcast messages. The trust recognised the need to dispense with jargon in order to do both of these. It felt that the final bid was too much about the 'what', with not enough of the 'how'.

The community trust valued and enjoyed forging partnerships, realising in the process just how confusing and chaotic the health service appears to those on the outside. It understood that there was value in developing a long-term view and that the community trust should not shy away from being controversial and visionary in this.

The voluntary sector was represented by 'Heartwell' which saw its main aim as improving the CHD situation, especially in relation to minority ethnic groups. It was keen to form partnerships with other organisations as vehicles to achieve this aim. The organisation built good partnerships with the acute trust, the council and the private sector organisation Lifestyle. However, it felt that it was not courted by the community trust. As a consequence it joined with the acute trust and Lifestyle in promoting the idea of a 'centre of excellence' for cardiac care and secondary prevention.

Initially Heartwell lobbied the health authority to ensure that CHD was near the top of the agenda in all the discussions regarding preparations for the proposal. The health authority agreed but, given the intensity of the negotiations between some of the other players, it became very difficult for Heartwell to make an impact. Towards the end of the first day, it formed a loose alliance with the black and minority ethnic people's forum to give it a greater voice. It also built a partnership with the local authority which was keen to involve Heartwell as a community group.

Later, Heartwell gained influence by working with the acute trust and Lifestyle to develop the 'centre of excellence' idea which began life as an idea for a 'health shop' to provide a service somewhere between a 'community health centre and a Citizens Advice Bureau'. Heartwell then approached the health authority for support for this idea as a delegate from this mini-project team. Interestingly, it was while Heartwell attended the steering group meeting on the second morning that the acute trust and Lifestyle decided to turn the idea into a cardiac centre with rehabilitation and leisure services on the side of it.

With hindsight, Heartwell decided that it should have resolved the dilemma between either ethnic health or CHD as its main focus, and then decided which specific projects it should contribute to or seek to influence. It came as some surprise to Heartwell that the health authority and the acute trust 'did not carry detailed visions of medical care in their heads'. Heartwell also felt that the community trust had its own vision which was not able to embrace the perspectives and aspirations of Heartwell, which had had to make most of the running in establishing partnerships with many of the statutory bodies.

The acute trust aimed to secure the future of secondary care in the context of the proposal to enhance health gain and tackle health inequalities. The trust was concerned not to dominate the debate about health gain. They believed that they had achieved their aims since the trust received support for its plans to redevelop and rationalise its hospital estate.

Throughout the simulation, the acute trust was resolved to point out the contribution it could make to, for example, CHD and minority ethnic health. During the radio programme the trust emphasised the importance of people getting as 'good a treatment as they should'. The acute trust continued to work hard to gain support for its bid to redevelop the hospital and create a cardiac centre, using money in part provided by Lifestyle. The trust was swift to spot the opportunity in the fact that nobody else was putting together a proposal for a substantial capital programme. It later proposed that a capital spend would be able to create a climate of sustainability. The trust did articulate its view that PFI may actually inhibit rather than promote development due to the complicated procedures for gaining PFI approval.

Overall the trust felt that the health authority could have done more to work with the GPs to develop a consensual vision of the future. With others, the trust players expressed surprise about the low-key role taken on by the primary care players – a truly primary care-led NHS seemed some way off. The trust concluded that (acute) trusts must and can talk to local authorities as they have a valuable input to make to NHS planning.

The private sector was represented by 'Lifestyle Health' which aimed to expand its business through identifying the need for new (and potentially profitable) services. In order to do this it planned to build solid partnerships with a number of agencies from which it would need support, particularly as it recognised that the success of its new ventures would probably depend upon the effectiveness of these partnerships.

At the end of the simulation, it was felt that Lifestyle had achieved its aims since, as the players put it, 'money talks' (and Lifestyle had money to invest). However, the organisation was left with a nagging concern that the overall success of its new ventures would depend so much upon the performance of its partners that it was taking a number of, possibly very costly, risks.

Lifestyle found its partners mainly in the acute trust and the voluntary organisation Heartwell. It did not receive a particularly warm welcome from the local authority – 'we don't want some elitist health club not accessible to local people' – while the GPs were suspicious of sharing information with a private organisation. Lifestyle thought that this could make evaluation of health gain very difficult.

After reflection, Lifestyle concluded that it would be aiming to measure itself against other comparable organisations (if it could find any such organisations) to develop its business approach. Lifestyle hoped that it had challenged the idea that all private organisations are 'baddies' – indeed it suggested that it might be more willing to find common ground than some of the more suspicious and parochial public sector bodies. Overall, Lifestyle felt that it was crucial to find ways of loosening the PFI guidelines. Introducing more multidisciplinary training would help to break down barriers between different agencies and, consequently, yield improved health gain.

The black and minority ethnic people's forum did not exist at the beginning of the simulation but emerged in response to the unfolding scenario. Its stated aim was to provide a focus for the health interests of black people and act as a pressure group on the health services. The group made its presence felt through articulate use of local media and skilful lobbying. It consistently asked for ethnic issues to be listened to and addressed. Some groups acted with interest and a desire to build bridges (including the local authority and voluntary sector) but others, such as the GPs, were uncertain of the group's status. Some players were disconcerted when confronted by an organisation which, whilst being very adept at using the media, would not quite 'play the game' of statutory services spending public money.

Learning and implications

Within the simulation the health authority emerged as the subject of very high expectations from all players. The health authority was seen, and saw itself as a key ringholder for health gain, balancing powerful interests, trying to give voice to the community and building partnerships, particularly with the local authority. These problems were acute, and the health authority's response was to adopt a facilitative style, trying to give air time fairly to all stakeholders. One of the benefits was that most stakeholders stayed on board with the project; another was that innovation was encouraged and grew in terms of specific proposals.

However, there were four problematic areas:

● There was a lack of vision and strategy with which to shape the bid and to balance short- and long-term goals. The tension between the pull of the bid and the focus on health gain was very hard to manage successfully.

● The facilitative approach adopted may have precluded the health authority from giving powerful leadership when it was needed.

● Communication and partnership with the regional office was poor.

● The health authority position on the primary care-led system seemed unclear – were the GP groups' competitors or collaborators? The accountability relationship between GPs and the health authority did not seem to be articulated – who was holding the GPs to account?

This raises a number of issues for consideration if health authorities are to improve their ability to deliver health gain for the population they serve. These include the need to:

● Formulate a development plan to put in place the arrangements and capabilities required to deliver national targets and health outcomes in a primary care-led system.

● Develop a model of managing inter-agency partnerships which is both facilitative and provides determined leadership. A model of facilitation which simply balances and develops relationships will not do. What is needed is a model that nurtures relationships but which is purposeful and outcome-focused. This will not be easy because, as the simulation showed, the partnerships involve powerful players (especially trusts and local authorities) whose weight and well thought-out aims can drown out smaller, less focused but important players, and which need robust handling to create win–win goals for the partners as a whole.

- Explore the role, support and development needs of key health authority players. The pressures on these people are likely to be acute, the challenges comparatively new and health authorities need to understand better what the development needs are.

The aims of the regional office in the simulation showed a focus on sound management and sound financial positioning, as well as a concern to encourage partnership and evidence-based clinically effective programmes. They appeared to pursue these aims with some rigour, and were clearly effective in contributing to the partnership-building which was such a central feature of the outcomes.

However, there were two areas in which the regional office performed less well:

- They were insufficiently proactive as they generally waited to be seen rather than to seek out dialogue, and, through adopting an Olympian approach, did not model the partnership behaviour which they wanted to engender. The support needs of the health authority may not have been perceived well enough nor effectively met. Their cover as 'neutral civil servants', while recognisable as a current model, may not have reflected the arm's-length relationship with central departments which Next Steps agencies generally have. There are other examples of senior civil servant behaviour – more proactive, strategic, forceful leadership – which could have served as models.

- They seemed to take on no responsibility at all for developing the primary care-led system, particularly when it was apparent that potentially powerful primary care players were limiting their own scope and purpose. The line of accountability and influence from GPs to regional office did not appear to operate. If the health authority was ambivalent in its relationship with the primary care players, and the regional office was not actively nurturing the primary care-led system, who was developing the primary care-led NHS?

This suggests a number of areas for further development at regional office level if they are to effectively deliver health gain through the functions they perform. These include the following recommendations:

- Senior regional managers will find it helpful to devote some attention to the role and managerial style required, given the change to their own status and the changes in the primary care-led system. In particular, regions should reflect on what degree of interventionism is appropriate to the circumstances.

- That regional offices assess the extent to which regions should be involved in partnerships with other agencies, such as local authorities. There are benefits and some costs in doing so, and there needs to be a reasonably clear understanding of what value can be added to the work of health authorities in this involvement. Areas about which collaboration could be considered should perhaps focus on pan-regional issues, such as cancers, cross-organisational learning or embedding health promotion in economic development programmes.

All health sector players said that they had developed fresh perceptions about the role of the local authority in shaping health improvement strategies, and that these were one of the most important of the learning experiences they would take away from the simulation.

HAROLD BRIDGES LIBRARY
S. MARTIN'S COLLEGE
LANCASTER

4. Research – health promotion and health gain in primary care

Design

The aim of the research was to identify the risks and opportunities to health promotion in the new primary care-led purchasing environment. The interviews were with GPs, members of primary health-care teams, and health authority managers, and explored the role and focus of health promotion in their work, and how this might change within the new primary care-led environment.

It explored issues including:

- The position of health promotion in current practice.
- What local data are collected, used and needed.
- What links there are with non-health-related agencies.
- What GPs and their teams see as their health promotion needs (in terms of products and services).
- How GPs and their teams see the position of health promotion in the context of primary care-led purchasing.

The planning and design of the research was undertaken with a small steering group comprising GPs, the West Midlands regional office and a director of the Birmingham Multifund.

The data collection consisted of:

- Semi-structured interviews with individual GPs.
- Focus group meetings in Primary Health Care Teams (PHCT) professional forums.
- Interviews with health authority managers.

The draft interview frame was tested through pilot interviews. Towards the end of the data collection phase, five GP interviews were carried out in London in order to test the West Midlands results for consistency. Most of the practices were located in the inner city area of Birmingham which has comparatively high deprivation rates, high unemployment and poor housing. London practices were in the west London area with similar social and economic profiles.

The data used in this report have been collected from about 70 people. Of these approximately half were involved through focus group sessions (practice nurses, district nurses and health visitors); the remainder were involved through interviews. Twenty GPs were interviewed, the majority of whom worked in the West Midlands. Five health authority commissioning managers and four practice managers were also interviewed.

Almost one-third of the GPs were from minority groups. Over 60 per cent of the GPs were fundholding, six were single-handers and the remainder were multi-partnered. Between them, the GP set covered an aggregate practice population of over 87,000 people. Every practice had a practice manager and a practice nurse; larger practices had more practice nurses. Almost all practices had attached a health visitor and a district nurse.

A small number of practices were located in more affluent areas of Birmingham, and had more socially and economically varied practices. Only one practice served a population with a majority of people from social class I and II and a high rate of home ownership. Most of the sample had a minority ethnic population of over 25 per cent of the practice population; two served populations where over 80 per cent of the people on the practice list were from minority ethnic groups.

One of the challenges confronting the researchers was the possibility that respondents would be unfamiliar with the proposals for a primary care-led NHS and the NHS Executive's proposed accountability framework. To overcome this problem, a briefing note summarising both was sent out to respondents, together with the interview frame, in advance of the interview.

Health promotion, in this project, was specifically defined as the process of enabling people to increase control over and to improve their health. In its broadest sense it is seen as the overlapping spheres of health education (e.g. stop smoking advice), health protection (e.g. healthy public policy) and disease prevention (e.g. breast screening).

Outcomes

What health promotion activities are currently carried out?

There was a considerable variation in the health promotion activities carried out by the various GP practices. These ranged from the opportunistic to the establishment of regular clinics and services and coherent communication programmes. Almost all the GP practices carried out opportunistic health promotion either within a consultation or within a clinic setting. Many of these activities were linked to chronic disease management of asthma, diabetes and hypertension, and all GPs offered clinics in these areas. Some offered additional clinics in areas such as smoking, weight control, exercise, diet and baby checking and weighing.

The services offered varied considerably between the practices. Three-year Well Person's services were the most popular. Individual sessions on diet, exercise and family planning were also offered. Three of the practices had an Asian dietitian who ran diet clinics for the Asian patients and gave individual sessions. Cancer screening services covering cancers of the cervix, testes, breast, and prostate gland, were available in some of the practices. One practice had carried out a campaign for cervical screening to reach a target of 96 per cent of their relevant practice population. This practice had also carried out another campaign about immunisation aimed at reaching a target of 90 per cent of the relevant population. Child health surveillance was offered by some of the practices, with some also offering ante- and postnatal care.

Family planning and contraceptive services were offered by several practices. One also included sessions on menopause and breast awareness within their family planning clinic. Two of the practices geared their contraceptive services specifically for young people, with free pregnancy tests and condom availability. One practice with a very high teenage pregnancy rate had all PHCT members trained in family planning in order to ensure that a comprehensive service was available to their young population.

Other services offered by individual practices included: hormone replacement therapy, HIV testing, drug addiction, geriatric screening. One practice that provided a dermatology service also had secondary care provision which included minor surgery. This service was offered to, and used by, other GPs in their surrounding area. Travel and travel-related immunisation services were also provided by some of the practices. A few had arranged weekly Citizens Advice Bureau sessions on their premises. Some practices communicated health education messages to their patients in the waiting room area by using videos and notices. One single-handed practice also had a lending library.

Much of the variation in services offered indicated GPs' responsiveness to the specific characteristics of their practice populations. For example, practice populations with high densities of Asians often offered services designed to reduce the onset of, or to manage, CHD. Others with high teenage pregnancy rates ensured that a comprehensive contraception service was available to their young groups. One inner-city practice had an open policy for the homeless.

Who delivers or 'leads' health promotion?

GPs and nurses were the main deliverers of health promotion. Generally GPs worked primarily on an opportunistic basis, but some shared and ran clinics with their practice nurses where much health promotion took place. Nurses delivered health promotion mainly through clinics.

GPs estimated an average of 15 to 20 per cent of their ten-minute consultations could be linked to health promotion. Practice nurses, however, were the key people delivering health promotion in the practice setting, spending between 20 and 100 per cent of their time doing so. Health visitors spent about 70 per cent of their time on it, but they concentrated their efforts on under-fives' child health. In one practice where there was an attached midwife the health visitor also provided antenatal services. District nurses focused their work on the elderly. They spent very little of their time (5 per cent) on health promotion.

Support services for health promotion, such as writing letters, making sure patients kept their appointments, and so on, was often provided by reception staff. Although practice managers were not directly involved in health promotion (the one exception related to someone who was a trained counsellor), they had important responsibilities in co-ordinating teams and activities and in ensuring that the appropriate administrative support was available.

Although most of the health promotion work is carried out by the nursing team, everyone (including GPs themselves) saw GPs as having the responsibility for leadership on these activities. The GP was the main gatekeeper for resourcing, and the main decision-maker for targeting, health promotion. That is not to say that others in the PHCT were not influential, especially the practice nurse and practice manager, but it was the GP to whom leadership was attributed. Practice nurses were often initiators of new health promotion activity, but had to balance a number of factors to get change, '. . . if you can't get past them [GPs] then there isn't a hope in hell's chance of doing anything . . . we have to make sure it doesn't take us from other work and is cost-effective – in particular with regard to time and effort, for example, there's no chance if we put in ten hours of work and only two stopped smoking'.

How are needs assessed?

GPs were asked what information they used for deciding what health promotion their practice populations needed. The question aimed to explore those situations in which the GP was not reacting to a presented problem or an opportunity presented during a consultation, but rather where the GP intended to be proactive on a health promotion issue.

Most GPs relied on their computerised practice data. Information on patients was collected in Well Person clinics by nurses, practice profiling (which was also nurse-led) and opportunistic screening of patients within consultations. These data generally consisted of Band Three information, such as smoking status, blood pressure, BMI (Body Mass Index), family history, etc., including data on diseases such as CHD, diabetes and asthma. These data enabled them to determine those individuals and groups with established disease and those at risk and hence target resources appropriately.

Paradoxically, many GPs did not place much value on their practice information systems and networks. Health authority commissioners in the interview set confirmed this, and ventured to explain this in terms of the poor coverage of the data, problems of accuracy and problems of quality. A further explanation might also be that some GPs place a low value on qualitative information which may not 'fit' with the medical model of evidence with which they had been trained. Interestingly, and by contrast, commissioning managers placed considerable weight on the informal information systems which practice nurses and health visitors provided through their contact with patients.

Five of the GPs felt they knew their patients and the surrounding area very well, and could therefore predict their patients' health needs. Two of the GPs had a high Asian population. They knew from national studies that this group was at a higher risk of diabetes and CHD, and therefore targeted health education at this group using issues such as diet, exercise and hypertension. Another GP had a high pregnancy termination rate amongst those under 14 years of age and a high incidence of chlamydia in his practice and had developed a comprehensive contraceptive service for young people. Only one GP volunteered that he consulted the public health annual report for information on the local population. GPs did not generally share their data between practices, though one GP expressed a need for information about neighbouring practices, suggesting that the health authority should take the responsibility of collating this information from the different practices and sharing the findings.

Other members of the PHCT and linked professionals were involved in assessing health promotion need. Of the three health-care professional groups, health visitors made the most extensive use of the different sources of information. These included census data, the health authority's Public Health Report, Department of Environment, Jarman scores, and information gained from play groups, voluntary groups and libraries. They also used national research data, and were, for example, aware of the higher incidence of diabetes in Asians and hypertension in the Afro-Caribbeans.

Neighbourhood studies carried out by student health visitors was another useful source of information for the PHCT. Needs were assessed during visits, meeting people on rounds and talking about health generally to individuals. Health visitors had also developed a suggestions box where patients could request health information. A 'patch' profile of the GP practice area was kept; health visitors had already started building a profile but covering a larger area than that of the GPs. The health visitors felt that their experience and these tools had enabled them to acquire an extensive knowledge of their local population. They shared this information amongst colleagues.

Although practice nurses had access to Band Three data and recognised this as potentially valuable, they did not examine the data as a matter of routine. Other pressing responsibilities, lack of time and lack of supporting staff made it difficult for them to do so. Ironically, health visitors (and district nurses), not being part of the core team, did not find it easy to have access to this information. They felt that the data provided to GPs by the health authority (the old FHSA) could be useful, but was not available unless specifically requested.

What materials are used?

Posters, leaflets and videos were by far the most popular means of informing the patient about health issues. Other materials used included magazines, books, cassettes and leaflets/guidelines that doctors had brought back from various training sessions. One practice brought in specialist professional nurses from drug companies to speak on subjects such as asthma and diabetes. One GP was considering public meetings and discussion groups as a means of communicating important health messages to his practice population.

The source of the material varied but came mainly from the specialist health promotion service, the HEA, the health authority and drug companies. When prompted, respondents said that material from the drug companies was of good quality, effectively targeted, usually geared to the clients' needs and freely available. Although most felt it was non-promotional, some practices 'customised' leaflets from drug and food companies, so that only those messages they wanted their patients to have were given to them.

Materials and guidelines obtained in postgraduate courses were quoted by some GPs as being very useful, and they were happy to share these with their patients. A small number of practices also produced material in-house; in most cases this was the practice leaflet, which included advice on minor illnesses and commonly asked questions.

GPs had an eclectic approach to providers of materials, accepting them from wherever they were available. The nurses were the main people responsible for ensuring a good supply of materials. Some of the GPs felt they could certainly do with more and better resources.

Perception about the effectiveness of health promotion

GPs were asked about their view of the benefits of health promotion in their practice. Responses were varied. There was a very small group of GPs who were not convinced that there were any benefits from the health promotion activities they carried out in their practices. One GP said that had he the option he would do no health promotion and a second doubted whether doctors should be responsible for people's attitudes and behaviour about their health. Another believed social rather than GP interventions were the more critical in improving public health. A small number of GPs said there was very little benefit for a lot of effort.

Over half the GPs felt there was benefit. Many believed that it was 'common sense – a small amount of effort now will help in the future . . . prevention is better than cure . . . it's good practice . . . it's much cheaper to prevent than try and pick up pieces afterwards . . . patients like it, feel cared for, they appreciate it . . . although I haven't perceived any immediate benefits, I anticipate them in the future, for example, a reduction in attendance for trivial problems, reduced drug bills and so on'.

GPs quoted a number of factors which they believed demonstrated that health promotion activity was effective. Some of these factors were local: 'I'm convinced because I have seen changes in the health of my patients over the last eight or nine years . . . I have a healthier list which will lead to a healthier nation . . . there is better control of disease, patients don't keep coming back, they are more aware of their physical health, have better control of their sugar levels, blood pressure, diabetes and so on . . . Immunisation programmes are having an effect because we see a reduction of TB, diphtheria, polio'. Others were national, ' . . . we know nationally smoking prevalence has reduced . . . using aspirin for primary and secondary prevention of heart disease reduces risk of cardiac failure'.

Patient feedback was an important source of effectiveness information: ' . . . my patients tell me, especially those that attend the Look After Your Heart classes'.

More efficient use of primary care resources was seen as one of the key benefits: ' . . . there are also fewer crisis events which is cost effective . . . reduced home visiting has saved money . . . less referrals and admission rates for asthmatics, diabetes, hypertension, because we manage them so well here we don't need to refer them to hospital'.

Future changes in the primary care-led NHS

Would the range of activities change?

Only a very small number of GPs felt that the range of health promotion activities they offered would increase within the new system. Resourcing was not the only factor. A key challenge was to adapt to new ways of working. Most, however, felt it would remain the same, the only change being to use health promotion in a more targeted way: ' . . . we'll focus on coronary care . . . become more focused, streamlined, evidence-based, and collect information of benefit to us . . . decide our own practice priorities and target resources there'. This attitude is consistent with one of the main purposes of the reforms: to achieve shifts in purchasing which are more sensitive to patient needs as seen by GPs.

One GP said he would consider having health professionals such as a dietitian or chiropodist in house as it would be more practical for patients, and another GP felt that now as 'our people have got used to doing health promotion, we will carry on doing it'.

However, most GPs saw resources as the main constraint on expanding the range of health promotion services, ' . . . financial constraints versus public need – the focus will be led by where the money is . . . cost benefits are more important to us as we are small businesses'.

Other constraints identified included:

- Physical capacity of buildings.
- Current levels of negative equity (among single-handers).
- Lack of motivation on the part of the patient.
- Difficulty in attracting medical staff into general practice.
- Persuading other partners to believe in health promotion.
- Lack of co-ordination in primary health care.
- The weight of tradition and training (historically a treatment service).
- Lack of appropriate skills, especially managing behavioural change.

Focusing on individuals and populations

GPs were presented with the following propositions:

- The focus of a GP's interactions with people was generally at the level of the individual patient.

- A primary care-led NHS implied that services needed to be commissioned at a population level.

- This might present GPs with a number of challenges, such as strategy development, information management and group or population needs assessment.

Most did not agree that GPs had only an individual focus. Many argued that some items of current work were already carried out with populations or groups in mind, in particular, activities relating to cytology smears, immunisation, diabetes and asthma. They pointed out also that the Health of the Nation targets were handled at the practice population level.

However, generally most agreed that leading commissioning and purchasing decisions at the population level would cause them difficulty. A minority felt that 'this was not, in any case, a doctor's responsibility to control a population's health – social change is required' or that it was not achievable, and that GPs should only focus on individual patients.

A few others felt that it was not useful to distinguish between individual and population, as the one led to the other. Also in some cases it was impossible to make this distinction, e.g. from the GP's point of view TB in an individual was a family problem.

Most were concerned that the individual/population focus involved a difficult tension. Respondents identified a number of constraints:

● Key health promotion target groups were located in schools and colleges, but GPs saw comparatively few under-16s in the surgery.

● The practice population size was too small to manifest accurate and meaningful trend data.

● Practice population data could be 'misleading; perinatal mortality would appear high in my practice but actually it's probably low across the district'.

Generally, GPs were willing to accept commissioning responsibility, resources permitting. They argued that a number of conditions needed to be in place, these included, good communication and effective co-ordination within the PHCT, effective sharing of information between health visitors and social workers, and the quality of the relationships with hospital doctors.

Information and strategy

GPs recognised that their ability to develop a strategic approach would be dependent on an effective partnership with the health authority, in particular with public health specialists. Although they would use their own practice-based information systems, considerable reliance would have to be put on public health reports and epidemiological and social information. Some GPs said that it would be important, though perhaps not easy, given 'patch pride', for GPs in adjacent practices to poll their practice data.

Some GPs would expect the health authority to be proactive, giving advice and supporting GPs in getting to understand their practice population's health needs and to identify trends. Many would expect the strategic lead to come from the health authority, 'they need to nudge us in the right direction'.

Developing healthy alliances and partnerships

It was suggested to GPs that the proposals for a primary care-led NHS placed a lot of weight on partnerships with health authorities, local authorities and communities. They were asked to what extent these already existed and what were likely to be the main success factors in developing such partnerships.

Almost all GPs were satisfied that the relationship with the new health authority was good, based primarily on the previous effective work between themselves and the old FHSA. A few had negative perceptions about the value of the health authority relationship; the most common criticisms among this group were that they were frustrated by what they perceived as the adversarial nature of the relationship and the 'power games' which they said were played.

A few once again felt that this was not an appropriate responsibility for GPs, 'the district is the right level for link work . . . every time a provider changes its managers it's a nightmare for us . . . it limits our purpose, which is the one-to-one with patients . . . I wouldn't get involved – it's a minefield . . . they are interested in populations, we in individuals'.

Some saw partnership-building as a project which required serious attention, and this meant that current levels of resourcing GPs precluded a role for them.

When looking beyond the traditional health service relationships, it became very clear that GPs felt entirely ill-equipped to be key players in partnership-building. For the majority, partnership-building had no tradition in general practice, and they were particularly unskilled in this area, 'I wouldn't know how to go about it'.

Part of the explanation might lie in the fact that many GPs generally have little or no connection with other agencies. Where they do, they experience difficulty in getting access to the individual people they want to talk with or getting what they want, 'when we ring they're never there . . . their staff are always changing . . . my request for social worker sessions in my surgery are consistently turned down'.

In spite of the general feeling of being unskilled to develop partnerships and the poor esteem in which other, especially social care, agencies are held, a large minority of GPs recognise the need for better relationships. This recognition has arisen in part because those GPs have had experience of local health campaigns and consider the role of local authorities to be an important one. Others want a primary care-led approach to work and see partnerships as an essential component of commissioning health improvement, 'a primary care-led NHS must free up GPs from consultations and surgeries and get them to think and act strategically . . . [it] should involve everyone at the primary care level'. This group of GPs frequently mentioned the need for 'a model of how we should talk to each other . . . we need a model from the government to give a push'.

The future priority of health promotion

GPs were asked how, if they had complete control over circumstances, they would position health promotion within their practices. The questioning aimed to explore what priority health promotion would have, and what, if any, the drivers of change would be.

With the exception of a couple of GPs, who said they would do no health promotion at all ' . . . because it spoils the doctor–patient relationship . . . GP fundholding is really about disease treatment', most GPs had a generally favourable attitude towards health promotion. Some were primarily motivated to do more health promotion because they got considerable job satisfaction from the effort to prevent disease and suffering through the education of individual patients. GPs would do more ' . . . because hospitals were doing so much less'.

Most GPs were able to identify those factors that would make them increase the priority of health promotion in their practices – if:

● patients wanted it;
● health promotion was resourced through ring-fenced funding;
● more and better skills were developed in the practice;
● greater support and priority was given by the health authority;
● it was targeted at specific groups of people and specific issues (e.g. smoking or teenage pregnancies), especially in high-risk groups and topics;
● it can be shown to be integral or linked to other GP work;
● help and support was available to keep practice members up to date.

The first of these factors was quoted the most often.

Interestingly, although a few mentioned evidence or effectiveness information as important factors, most did not until prompted. Formal evidence of effectiveness of health promotion interventions did not appear to be a crucial factor in the minds of GPs in deciding the priority of health promotion activity. GPs were satisfied with their own practice evidence of benefit. It is not clear whether, for many GPs, availability of resources and incentives are more important in increasing the priority of health promotion than a proven benefit of a health-promoting activity – or, whether effectiveness evidence carries little weight because so little of it is known by, or communicated to, GPs.

GPs sourced their information about health promotion primarily through contact with peers – either from public health or through their participation in postgraduate (PG) seminars and other PG forums. Both were seen as important. Public health specialists were seen as important partners, as sources of quantified data and consultants with advice in how to understand local variations in need. PG forums helped GPs keep up to date with effectiveness assessments.

If additional health promotion funding was made available, GPs said they would spend it on assessing health promotion needs in their practices, on recruiting an additional practice nurse and on training practice nurses and health visitors.

What types of evidence would be valued?
GPs' responses generally showed a bias towards 'hard' evidence (e.g. randomised trials, quantitative data). This was particularly pronounced in those who were sceptical of the benefits of health promotion. The latter group said that they

were unlikely to pay any regard to other types of evidence. This response contrasts sharply with the findings in the section 'How are needs assessed?', where the evidence-based approach seemed to have such a low priority.

None the less, many GPs were either open-minded or positive about 'soft' forms of evidence. They specifically mentioned the usefulness of local lifestyle surveys, small-scale local studies, and the monitoring of local news media as valuable. At the same time GPs were often irritated at the routine collection of data, such as height and weight, without what they considered as a clear indication of their usefulness.

Practice-based data would continue to be considered valuable. This included 'patient feedback', informal audits carried out by the practice nurse, PGEA (Postgraduate Education Allowance) events and practice information systems.

GPs were divided about the value of national targets and priorities, which the GP Accountability Framework specifically mentions as an area of responsibility for GPs involved in purchasing decisions.

One said, 'most GPs are cynical about the Health of the Nation and feel it's the government's agenda and not ours'. But others considered that national targets 'help us focus, [although] we do need to break these down at the local level'.

Implications

Information and evidence

Health visitors interviewed showed that they were used to using a wide range of sources of information, and formed their judgements by balancing hard and soft, qualitative and quantitative information. They, together with practice nurses, are keen to learn about what works in terms of health promotion interventions. Their receptiveness is an important opportunity. However, health visitors are often not considered core members of the PHCT, and development work will be required to resolve problems of territorialism and difficulties in sharing information.

Although all the practices interviewed had invested in developing local information systems, not all GPs placed value in these. Many GPs also placed a low value on 'soft' or qualitative information. Interestingly, much of this soft information, in particular that captured in the experience of practice nurses and health visitors, would in a commercial context, be considered an essential part of the process of gaining marketing intelligence. Some GPs appear to exhibit self-limiting behaviour here by an over-reliance on medical models of evidence. Development work is required with practice teams to enhance the role of practice nurses and health visitors, and to persuade GPs to develop a richer model of evidence without losing the strong empirical orientation with which their medical education has endowed them.

GPs and PHCTs are receptive to the use of a wide range of health promotion materials – these could include written, visual/video and aural media as well as multi-media communication. But they respond best to materials which they perceive to be focused on specific topics, risk factors or diseases. They like material to be well targeted, and therefore highly appropriate for specific population or disease groups. And they want material which is accessible, that is, well written and presented. Materials production therefore needs to be preceded by a thorough understanding of general practice perceptions of what constitutes 'good' health promotion materials and communication media. This will mean gathering effective marketing intelligence and creating effective marketing strategies for general practice.

Developing partnerships

It has become widely acknowledged within the NHS, and especially within the health promotion community, that inter-agency partnerships are an essential building block in the achievement of health outcomes. While health outputs (e.g. coronary bypass grafts, Look After Your Heart campaigns, dietitian interviews) can be controlled and produced directly by a health organisation, health outcomes (e.g. a reduction in the rate of cardiac disease in a given population) can only be achieved over a longer-term timescale and through a multiplicity of partners, including individuals or groups of 'patients'.

The research evidence indicates strongly that GPs are extremely diffident about their capacity to build such partnerships. This does not mean that they are not interested in doing so. The experience of Roundabout showed that, following exposure to situations in which partnership-building took place, GPs and PHCT members said that learning about partnership-building was one of the most useful lessons they took away with them from the simulation. For GPs and PHCTs to perform well on this issue, they will need investment in developing the appropriate skills and contact networks. The skills will include: understanding the goals and roles of other agencies, negotiating in a strategic context, being able to link health and social care, sharing information and using shared information, using decision-support tools and group working.

One set of partnerships which are particularly unfamiliar for most GPs are relationships with local community organisations and other local groups. Relationships here are one of the most difficult areas of work for the NHS, and it is not easy to find districts where these relationships are working very well. GPs are therefore wisely wary and their diffidence justified. However, these relationships are also essential and unavoidable in carrying out any strategic purchasing or commissioning role. Developing relationships with local community organisations, and in health terms this often means developing local community organisations, therefore represents a significant development challenge for GPs and PHCTs.

Influencing behaviour in general practice

Three key variables in the behaviour of GPs have emerged. First, it is clear that the level of resourcing for health promotion will be a key factor in GPs' decisions about what to provide and what to purchase. There appears to be some support for ring-fencing, because GPs are likely to regard ring-fenced objectives as if they are contractual obligations. However ring-fenced topics need to be seen by GPs to be necessary and appropriate in order to avoid the irritation which some aspects of the banding system caused. The research did not set out to explore this question in detail and the potential effects of ring-fenced funding need further investigation.

A second key variable which is likely to affect GP behaviour is the skill pool which is available to them. Here there seems to be considerable scope for external agencies to offer help. There is a receptiveness in general practice for development initiatives. GPs have already a tradition for assistance in 'facilitation', and they see further development as an extension of this tradition. Practice nurses and other members of the PHCT are obvious targets for this development effort – they already meet in informal professional forums, have a history of education and are keen to learn. As already mentioned, health visitors should also be important targets for development, but this development needs to go hand-in-hand with work to improve the connections between health visitors and the PHCT.

Finally, people in general practice are highly dependent on external providers for their information needs. Members of the PHCT are generally likely to be receptive to well-targeted information, especially about effective interventions. Information flows to general practice would benefit if they were co-ordinated; confusing or conflicting information, due perhaps simply to differing presentation formats, would be disliked. Working with, and perhaps through, in some instances, the health authority's public health function, is likely to ensure successful communication of information about risk, morbidity, good practice and effectiveness.

Levers for change

Relationships and partnerships are likely to be both an essential element of effective working for health improvement and a way of levering change in general practice. As the Roundabout simulation also showed, investing in developing partnerships, in particular in relation to the health authority and local authority, can stimulate GP interest and awareness. But GPs feel particularly ill equipped for this and will need considerable support. Such partnerships need a robust framework to guide the partners, especially in maintaining a focus on the purpose or desired outcome of the partnerships.

One of the main drivers of change could be the provision of information about the effectiveness of specific health promotion interventions. The research shows that evidence is not the most critical motivator of GP behaviour. However, this may well be because in the absence of appropriate, focused, targeted effectiveness information, GPs rely on a range of other indicators, including their own logic and belief systems. Other factors, including the tradition and training of GPs, the influence of postgraduate education, the receptiveness of practice nurses and health visitors and the trajectory of national NHS thinking on this issue, are likely to combine to enable evidence-based initiatives to have a powerful impact on general practice. Information about the effectiveness of interventions is unlikely to be created simply from the spread of good practice, valuable though this is. What is required is focused research and dissemination through effective communication programmes by national agencies. These might be tasks for bodies such as the HEA, perhaps working collaboratively with the NHS and its research and development directorate.

Peer influence is likely to be an important lever. This might be effected through the identification and dissemination of good practice, the targeting of demonstration projects and through postgraduate education forums.

In summary, there are a number of important issues that need further consideration:

- GPs' central involvement in planning and service development, in addition to their more traditional role as a service provider, is creating some obvious strains. They also have difficulties in shifting their perspectives towards a more strategic direction, operating in more 'team' oriented ways, and recognising the opportunities and demands of partnership working. They will need support and possibly continuing training to meet these demands. Few GPs have received any management development and although there have been many advances as a result of fundholding initiatives, the recent Audit Commission report reflects the great range in quality and competence in these areas.

- Closer links must be forged between GPs, members of the PHCT and health promotion specialists. There are dangers of distancing, and all that this entails in terms of loss of confidence, an inability to build effective partnerships, and the predictable response from GPs, that health promotion is all essentially common sense and 'they don't see why they shouldn't have the money and manage it themselves'.

- There are a wide range of new localised arrangements emerging, including multi-funds, locality commissioning groups, GP forums, and joint service and planning arrangements with social services. There is a pressing need to explore both the demands on GPs and practice managers of these changes, and a requirement to assess their different levels of effectiveness.

- The health authorities are 'required to support GPs in both their primary care provision and fundholding capacities through the provision of advice, investment and training'. From most GP perspectives involved in the project, this was often an unclear process and appeared incremental rather than offering a planned programme of development. GPs, and others involved directly in primary care, need to understand the plans of their authorities and consider ways of informing the strategic decisions that will guide investment and priorities in respect of their development.

- Although the GP is a crucial figure in the development of primary care centred approaches to planning and delivering services to achieve health gain, there are many other key people and interests that need to be considered. There are dangers that their needs for contact, recognition and development may be obscured by the amount of attention that is currently being given to GPs.

5. Action learning sets

Design

Three multi-agency, multi-professional action learning sets were established as part of the Joint Venture. These groups were tasked with exploring and developing their collective experience in commissioning for health gain. Within this framework participants developed their own agenda and ways of working. Each set was supported by a facilitator from OPM. The role of the facilitator was to enable the group to develop its own leadership capability to work together effectively to achieve its goals.

The work of the learning sets closely paralleled typical processes of inter-agency working for health gain in the context of a primary health care-led NHS. The groups were interested in finding out what kinds of changes and innovations in the commissioning environment could lead to greater health gain for the population – such as moving beyond responses to ill health, and focusing on local activities within the context of the Health of the Nation and other relevant policy drivers. Common issues that emerged were:

● An initial search for a definitive formulation of 'health gain' was replaced with the recognition that 'good enough' definitions based on *mutual exchange and understanding* were sufficient to provide a basis with which to move forward.

● Different agencies have different policy imperatives and use different terminology. It was therefore important to identify areas of *synergy and overlap* rather than seeking to insist that all agencies act in the same way.

● Although there was evidence available to inform commissioning decisions, it was not easy to judge its reliability or *transferability to local settings*.

● Sharing examples of local projects and initiatives was helpful in developing an enhanced understanding of ways to create *health gain-related change*.

● Jointly developing *generalised models* that capture the processes and information requirements of commissioning for greater health gain proved a substantial aid to knowledge synthesis and shared understanding.

The Process

Getting started

The action learning sets began in November 1995 with a meeting of the members of all three sets – about thirty people, who were all involved in some way in developing commissioning for health gain. They included people in regional offices of the NHS Executive, health authority commissioners, public health consultants, medical advisers, GPs, health promotion specialists, social services managers, primary care managers and environmental health and other health specialists in local authorities. In this respect each learning set modelled the diversity of roles and agencies in the field but, because people came from different places and did not know each other at the start, their participation in the learning sets did not carry the 'baggage' of local politics. This turned out to be an important facet of their work together.

The first meeting established agreed ways of working and a forward agenda for each of the learning sets. Thereafter the sets met separately once a month until May 1996, when they came together again to share and extend their learning at a one-day conference.

The people who took part in the learning sets brought with them issues, concerns and puzzles from their field experience which they felt could be addressed through the project, and which therefore shaped the initial agenda of the learning sets. Amongst these, the most frequently expressed were:

● A recognition of the importance of inter-agency work in achieving health gain and a wish to learn how to do it better.

● Support for the development of health strategies which are patient-focused and encompass primary care, community care and continuing care.

● A desire, in particular from non-NHS employees, to have a better understanding of the ways in which health workers operate.

● A significant understanding of the applicability and practical relevance of health promotion, health improvement and health gain to their organisation's goals.

● A concern over how best to manage priority setting and shifts in resourcing, given the high level of investment in existing patterns of services.

There was widespread recognition that the world was changing fast and that, while there were no simple answers, it was up to people like themselves who had influence and the ability to direct resources to devise new ways of addressing these problems and issues in order to achieve better health outcomes.

Stage one – finding a common language

In the initial agenda setting discussion, members of the sets brainstormed the range of issues and a range of terminology, including 'health', 'health gain', 'health promotion', 'health improvement' and 'health development', all of which evidently meant different things to different people. The first urgent task was to find a way of talking to each other and being understood. Consequently each learning set (quite independently) embarked on a process of developing shared definitions of these key ideas.

A first and obvious question was 'whose definition of health gain?' Was it that of the patient, or the clinician, or should it be based on a wider population perspective? Discussion covered the many factors that can be combined to create an holistic definition, such as the relevance of age and a mind, body, spirit nexus. Too often, it was felt, there is an over-focus on 'body' to the relative exclusion of other factors. Definitions based on notions of ill health (for example, counting coronaries) were felt to be too simple and not particularly meaningful. At the other extreme definitions such as that provided by WHO were seen to be too broad and all embracing, such that everything becomes an aspect of 'health'. Particularly for those working outside the health service, this was seen as a difficulty in that definitions of 'health' have a tendency to broaden out to encompass all aspects of physical, mental and spiritual wellbeing. While this may in some sense be true, it can make discussion and development confusing since little or nothing is excluded. Participants became aware that other service areas (housing, environment, social services and so forth) have little difficulty identifying their contribution to 'health' because of this broad definition. Traffic in the other direction is less easy to identify.

Eventually participants took refuge in Heisenberg's uncertainty principle, paraphrased as 'the more you try to pin things down the less accurate the definition becomes'. It was agreed that different definitions serve different purposes; the important thing is to have the conversation, understand each other's perspectives and through this create a shared sense of direction. An adequate lay definition was considered to be 'adding years to life and life to years for everyone'. Alternatively, health gain can be considered as 'a term used to describe an improvement in health status and/or the quality of life that results directly or indirectly from the consumption of health care'.

Summarising these discussions, it was felt that:

● To the extent that 'health gain' continues to be a useful concept, its main value is in providing a clear outcome focus to guide commissioning. Importantly, this appreciation in itself can be effective in modifying individuals' approaches to commissioning by encouraging consideration of the extent to which different choices or priorities contribute to health outcomes.

● At the same time, 'health gain' as a driving concept has little currency outside health service arenas – notably so in local authority contexts where, for example, Local Agenda 21 has more saliency. Consequently, in all multi-agency settings the most important consideration is to ensure the necessary conversations take place and an adequately agreed and understood definition is arrived at. This will help to overcome any potential sense of health service 'colonialism' and give sufficient acknowledgement to other, related, concepts and definitions. The notion of 'health and social gain' has value in this respect.

By this stage participants were becoming more interested in discussing the contributions different agencies, both individually and in partnership, could make to the health gain agenda. In the search for a bridge between definitions and effective practice, the model representing health gain 'in the round'

(Figure 1), was used to map the relative location of the efforts of health authorities (HA), public health medicine(PH), health promotion specialists (HP), GPs and others.

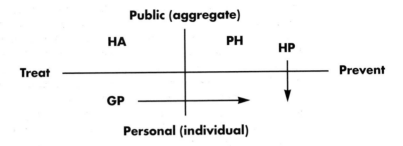

Fig. 1. Health gain 'in the round'

It was noted that the current changes mean that 'traditional' positions of agencies and specialisms on this grid may be shifting, in response to the enhanced importance of PHCTs, particularly that of health promotion specialists. One local example is illustrated in Figure 1. Whilst this particular pattern may not be replicated in every situation it does show clearly that it is not necessary or helpful for everyone to occupy the same space, nor to attempt to persuade others to do so. In other words the (perhaps) natural desire to attempt to persuade other agencies and professionals to be more like oneself, whilst understandable, will not necessarily lead to greater health gain. What is more useful is to try to ensure that all the ground is covered and the efforts of different agencies mesh and reinforce one another at the interfaces.

Stage two – sharing experience and practice

The learning sets established a common practice of sharing articles, slides, references and local experiences which were offered for discussion and scrutiny by other members of the learning set. There was considerable enthusiasm on the part of individuals to share sources of information which they had personally found useful, but it was apparent that others found it less easy to transfer learning in this format to their own situation. It was often difficult to be sure either about the status or the interpretation of evidence and, even when this was reasonably certain, it was difficult to know how best to use it to affect the decisions of key resource holders. Through these discussions participants developed greater awareness of two essential aspects of commissioning for health gain. Firstly, the value of sharing different case examples of innovation in order to learn how others had undertaken successful change projects and secondly, the need to build more comprehensive models of commissioning processes that take into account a wider range of factors and processes than are commonly included. In particular, it was clear that a great deal of mutual learning occurred when participants had the opportunity to interrogate local examples of change, such that they were able to understand the change process from the perspectives of different agencies, and the tools and techniques of change management which had been successfully used. A selection of the examples of innovation and change discussed are shown below.

An integrated primary care initiative

The relative isolation of this total purchasing pilot means the practice (list size 10,000) is particularly suitable for trying out new ideas. The practice seeks to achieve an holistic approach to care. Since it is in a 'designated area of need' a range of grant funding is available including, possibly, from the Rural Development Commission, which would be a 'first' for that agency. Very close links with social services are considered essential, and there is a single community nursing team. The design of the new, custom-built centre is central to developing new ways of working and has been developed through multi-agency discussions. The vision of the future includes integrated appointments systems, cross-referring and access to other agencies' databases. Building and extending local relationships has been an important part of the process which offers its own gains beyond the physical development of the centre. One piece of advice to others contemplating a similar development would be to go for private finance – this has not been done here.

This initiative is based on a belief in the value of a physically integrated primary and social care facility in an area of low population density. A similar initiative in urban areas might require different means to achieve similar ends.

Improving prescribing in primary care

This project was intended to reduce symptomatic prescribing and increase disease-specific prescribing, based on the belief that generic prescribing is a good indication that GPs actually know what they are doing. Incentives were offered to poor performing practices during a three-month monitoring period. The consequent increase in generic prescribing also gave cost savings of £60,000 for an incentive of £28,000. The positive trend continued – once behaviour changed there seemed to be little recidivism. The key drivers appeared to be education coupled with financial incentives plus, no doubt, a bit of Hawthorne effect. Whilst this change is in itself only a proxy for health gain, it could be tracked through, for example, reductions in emergency admissions for asthma.

In this example a highly proactive approach, backed with financial incentives, has both created behavioural change and saved money.

Developing counselling services for mental health patients in primary care

● A presentation to the GP board convinced them that mental health counselling should neither be done by GPs nor mean an automatic referral to secondary services. Funding for the initiative was shared between the health authority and practice budgets; the difficulties arose in implementation.

● The GP consortium did not have the status to be the employer so two individual practices agreed to take it on, but with only one reporting relationship. The consortium manager and the mental health adviser were also closely involved.

● The counsellor was not prepared to be self-employed and this option would in any case have been more expensive.

- The GP host had to be set up as a provider so that overheads could be recharged.

- The counsellor needs support (beyond supervision) but it is not immediately clear where this comes from.

This is an illustration of the fact that apparently simple, good ideas can uncover a number of challenges to be overcome in implementation. Persistence and a willingness to explore untried options are necessary.

Decision-making in local communities

- In this example, agencies had genuinely handed over the decision-making power to local communities. They found that:

  - if the community is involved they are more effective in getting sponsorship and support from local businesses;
  - the community has different ways of structuring health gain activities and it can be difficult for agency staff to accept different views;
  - it may be a useful principle to insist that agency staff are outnumbered at meetings involving communities or the public;
  - community members are very happy with a health gain approach based on determinants of health rather than a medical model.

The discussion of specific projects led into a broader discussion of the utility of projects in general as a means for moving forward on the health gain agenda, with the following general observations:

- The evaluation of small projects is expensive, often not done properly, or only done on the basis of small amounts of money such as joint finance.

- There is a danger that one project will have to bear the weight of too many expectations and, potentially, fail under this weight.

- Big clinical trials may represent a 'purer' approach but they can be too narrow in their focus to capture the complexities of health gain.

- It is ethically difficult to have a control group in terms of 'withholding' services.

- Projects can easily be non-strategic, as well as focusing on major change.

- A 'political' approach offers a better prospect of viability than one which is primarily 'economic' or 'clinical' – look for the win–win agenda.

Difficulties arise at the point when it is attempted to evolve good projects into mainstream practice. It sometimes seems as if it is more important to have good projects on the go than to work out how good practice is going to be made universal. This specific difficulty raises wider questions about the most effective ways of creating and sustaining fundamental change.

Stage three – leading and managing change

Each learning set moved on from sharing and exploring good practice examples to considering the more general and universal lessons for creating health gain-related change.

One set developed a SWOT (strengths/weaknesses/opportunities/threats) analysis for health gain (Figure 2) as a means of better understanding the factors that are already working for health gain-related change and which are more likely to work against it, thus providing a possible agenda for action.

Opportunities Broader influence. More sophisticated presentation. Develop latent interest. Developing ownership. Incentives. Targeting.	**Weaknesses** Lack of health input into local authority decisions. History of illness-based NHS. Vested interests in services. Lack of accepted methods for measuring outputs. Image of health promotion. No leadership for health gain
Strengths Existing relationships. Commitment, dedication, experience. Economic argument.	**Threats** Public perception of disinvestment. Errors due to lack of information on the effect of health decisions. Politics and politicians. Professionals. Scientific criticism. Short-termism.

Fig. 2. A SWOT analysis for health gain

Whilst not everyone might agree with the details of this SWOT analysis, the challenges it throws up are a good illustration of some of the difficulties which need to be overcome in the interests of achieving greater health gain. Some are particularly worth noting. For example:

● The need to involve the public in these debates, since without this members of the public can find it difficult to see health service changes as other than hospital closures, and hence do not give their support to the health gain agenda.

● It is unclear where the leadership for health gain resides. It is well known that health authorities are under considerable pressure to act as the co-ordinating mechanism for all local initiatives. There is therefore both an issue of capacity and the question of whether this is best or only a means of co-ordinating progress towards health gain, given that its achievement will depend on inter-agency and multi-professional collaboration.

● The need to disinvest in existing patterns of services in order to reinvest in new ones.

This last point was given attention by another learning set who considered ways of affecting traditional patterns of purchasing by contrasting traditional and marginal approaches to the analysis of need and provision. They identified a fundamental dilemma (Figure 3) in that health authorities are being encouraged to make better use of prevention techniques in relation to CHD, but at the same time they should not redirect resources away from surgical interventions.

Many health authorities have already put considerable effort into . . . the prevention and treatment of CHD. In practice, however, the daily work of health authority staff is often dominated by the demands of the annual contracting cycle and the provision of in-patient care. In terms of further health gains . . . the case for shifting the focus of commissioner attention more towards preventive forms of care requires careful examination.

In the immediate future, better use of secondary prevention techniques offers a particularly important route towards achieving reductions in mortality. Commissioners should aim to ensure such opportunities are fully exploited in their districts. They should also consider the extent (and likely cost) of the health gains to be derived from improvements in services for people suffering heart attacks, and from prevention programmes.

However, recognition of the current need to realign the balance of commissioning activity must not be taken to imply that commissioners should direct resources away from such areas as the provision of coronary artery bypasses, or fail to invest more money to satisfy unmet need for revascularisation. Under-provision of either interventional cardiology or cardiac surgery is likely to cause concern and distrust among health-care providers and service users alike, rather than promoting informed agreement and concerted action on the best overall ways to reduce the pain, disability and death caused by CHD.

Fig. 3. The dilemma for health authorities

This dilemma, summarised in Figure 4, appears to require some modification to the traditional approach (Figure 5), particularly in its over-concentration on short-term concerns and lack of attention to effectiveness and cost-benefits. In the traditional model an assessment of need is followed, inevitably, by a recognition of insufficient resources to meet this need. Subsequent prioritisation of resource allocation against need should – but this cannot be guaranteed – lead to greater health gain.

Investing for the future

Pay now – gain later

Reduce treatment – improve health

Fig. 4. The dilemma – summarised

- Equates need with illness or disability
- Equates health gain with cure or reduced disability
- Encourages prioritisation on basis of size of problem
- Ignores cost-benefit issues
- Ignores effectiveness criteria
- Encourages concentration on short-term benefits
- Squeezes out 'soft items'

Fig. 5. The traditional approach

Conversely, a marginal analysis (Figures 6 and 7) works only with those areas where service changes are being made. It is therefore cost neutral and should encourage a multi-agency and outcome-focused approach. The limitation is that only a few service areas can be dealt with in one commissioning round, but these should be addressed fully and effectively to maximise health gain in these areas. It is likely to take longer but there can be more confidence that real improvements in health should ensue. The key question raised by this discussion and its associated dilemmas is how is disinvestment in traditional treatment regimes to be 'bought out' in the shorter term in order to enable its replacement with greater attention to prevention? Whilst there are no simple answers the use of a marginal approach is perhaps more realistic and more fruitful, given the current commissioning context.

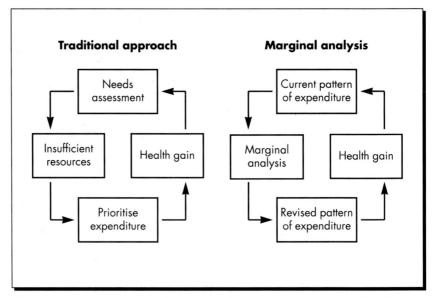

Fig. 6. Comparison between the traditional approach and a marginal analysis

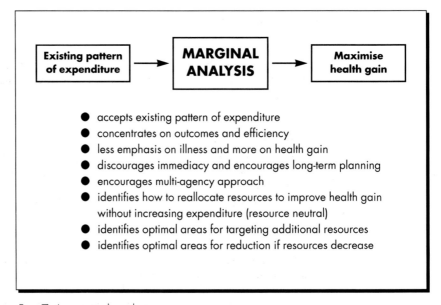

Fig. 7. A marginal analysis

The quest for a simple model to capture the essential elements of health gain led to the development of the partnership–evidence–change triangle (Figure 8). Below we give one field example of these elements in practice which is particularly interesting because it involves a partnership between a social services community care team for older people and a primary care total purchasing pilot.

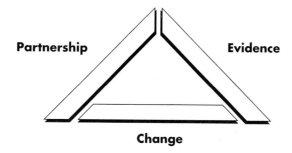

Fig. 8. Achieving health gain

Commissioning for health gain–partnership – a case example

The partners:

● Primary health-care team – total purchasing pilot.

● Social services–community care – older people and disability.

● Health authorities.

● Community health council.

Aim

● Use the total purchasing pilot to explore the boundaries and overlaps between primary health care and social services care for the patients in the practice:

○ to find common ground;
○ to maximise effectiveness of current resources;
○ to create opportunities to influence each other's purchasing;
○ to create an opportunity for developing team working to achieve a 'seamless' service for patients;
○ to try out a pilot that would influence the services city-wide.

The future developments

● Revision of a screening card for those aged over 75 years and matching with local authority referral information.

● Joint appointment of community co-ordinator post for one year to facilitate access for patients to:

○ health promotional activities;
○ social services resources;
○ voluntary sector/community resources services;
○ liaise, educate, record and make recommendations for future development.

Supervised, supported and trained by social services, based in the practice and funded by them. The main features of this piece of work are:

- A recognition of the need to move beyond working parties and create effective action.

- The clear intention to provide a 'seamless' service for patients.

- A willingness to influence and be influenced by each other's purchasing intentions.

- A shared wish to maximise the use of current resources.

- Mutual access to each other's databases in the interests of patients, and revision of information recording formats to ensure compatibility across agencies.

- The introduction of community co-ordinators who are trained and supervised by social services, but located in and funded by GP practices.

- Facilitation of patients' access to a full range of services, including health promotion, social services and voluntary sector services.

Through the work of the learning sets there was an increasing recognition that a key factor in moving forward towards greater health gain was resourcing the change process itself through, for example, the development of change management skills, and more accessible evidence. One example of how this might be managed was a health strategy co-ordinator role, a concept developed by one of the learning sets. This concept was explored by asking what skills were needed to be effective in health gain work. Participants worked in pairs to generate a range of ideas which were then listed and prioritised through a visible voting procedure. Exercises of this nature are valuable in creating multidisciplinary involvement and demonstrating overtly democratic processes towards agreement. As such they can be usefully transferred into local settings which are facing similar developmental issues.

Here the key skills were considered to be:

- An ability to influence others and the public to act to achieve health gain.

- An ability to identify needs and areas of maximum impact for health gain.

- An ability to seek solutions once needs are identified.

- An ability to lever resource shifts out of less health gain areas.

- Clarity about the difference between commissioning and purchasing.

- An ability to focus on services which address causes of health damage rather than symptoms.

- A focus on providing services known to contribute to health gain.

In addition, such people would need to be able to 'translate' identified needs and problems into health gain frameworks and do this using language understood by the audience one is seeking to influence. In this sense an effective agent for health gain might well be working 'under cover'.

Stage four – models of effective commissioning

The final stage in this process, for the time being at least, was for members of the learning sets to consolidate their learning by developing new models that capture better ways of responding to health needs and achieving health improvement which go beyond health service provision. This is an elaboration of the partnership–evidence–change triangle (Figure 8) and includes the integration of health promotion into total purchasing plans. Two models of effective commissioning, developed by the learning sets as examples of the kind of processes which should be involved, are shown below.

The process model

This model places most emphasis on developing a clear health gain strategy, based on shared vision and values and accurate information. It was felt that a key to success would be robust information, as shown in Figure 9.

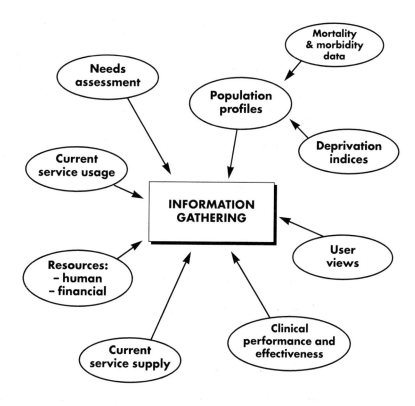

Fig. 9. Information requirements

A process model was chosen because it provides:

● a whole system approach;
● a multi-agency approach;
● a tool to talk to stakeholders;
● a means to identify gaps, to structure information and formulate questions.

The development of this approach to a more detailed process map for instance in addressing high blood pressure would look like Figure 10.

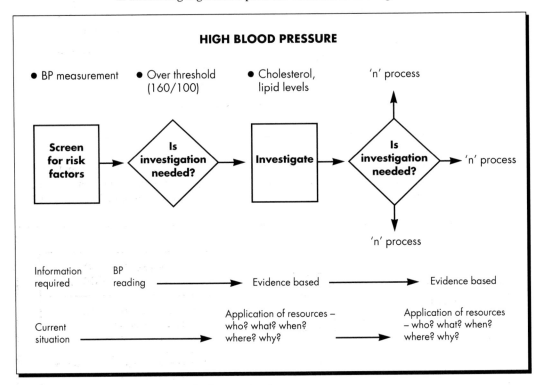

Fig. 10. A worked example of a process map

In considering the model, the group decided it must have the following characteristics:

● Evidence-based.
● Outcomes-focused.
● Promoting a 'learning organisation' environment/culture.
● Helping management of resources and priorities.
● Balancing/managing multi-agency expectations/demands.
● A whole system approach.
● A process which can generate/gain key stakeholder commitment.

The key areas that the model would need to address are represented in Figure 11.

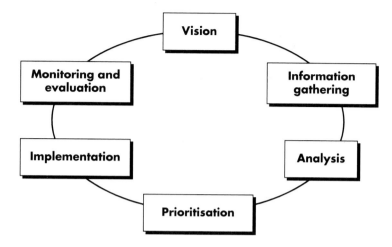

Fig. 11. Elements of the model

Consideration of the vision would require a reading of the environment, an agreement on the underpinning values and principles that would lead to a clear vision at an individual and population level. This is represented in Figure 12.

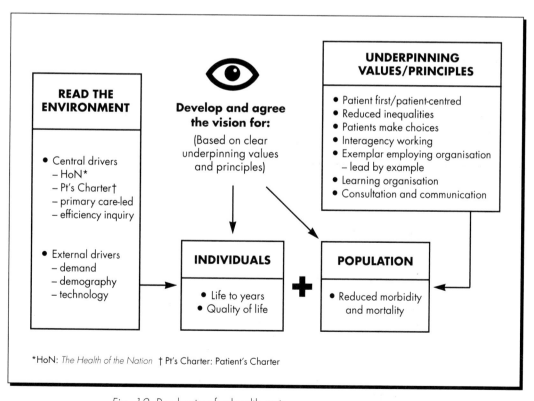

Fig. 12. Purchasing for health gain

The 'Daisy' model

The 'Daisy' model introduces more detailed consideration of the nature of partnerships, evidence, tactics and the need for evaluation (Figure 13). It thus raises some useful questions which can aid the planning of a health gain 'campaign'.

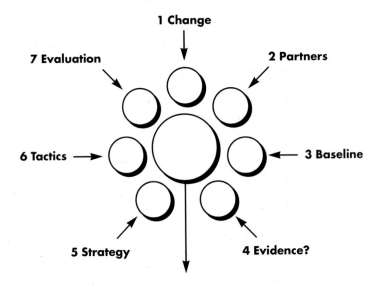

Fig. 13. 'Daisy' model for achieving health improvement

Achieving health improvement
● Establish need for change.
● Collect necessary evidence.
● Identify partners and forge relationships.
(Not necessarily in that order.)

Who are your partners?
● Active partners – other health agencies.
● Passive partners – e.g. community groups.
● Investigate their agendas.
● Establish common ground.

Where are we now?
● Identify shared:
  ○ baseline information;
  ○ targets for improvement;
  ○ constraints (financial, political, etc.);
  ○ risks.

● I'll show you mine if you show me yours . . .

What is the evidence for change?

- Is it robust?
- Will it command respect?
- Is it recent?
- Is it relevant?

(Not all research is good research.)

When summarising the main indicators of good practice in commissioning for health gain the following features were considered to be essential:

- Underpinned by research and evidence-based data.
- Robust information is the key to informing good purchasing practice.
- Ensure you can evaluate (using qualitative and qualitative measures).
- Promote multi-agency involvement.
- Look for 'simple' solutions that are practical and can be implemented locally.
- Involve the client group in decisions about purchasing.
- Ensure the approach is consistent with national policy and local strategy.
- Look for opportunities to influence the process from the provider side.
- Encourage innovation and risk-taking.

These approaches have been tested and refined by participants in the learning sets. Whilst they should not be viewed as the definitive or only way forward, they do embody both a wealth of practical experience and a willingness to expose individual ideas to the rigour of others' thinking. As such they can provide useful frameworks to stimulate local innovation and change when coupled with the energy and commitment of those in a position to influence the future shape of commissioning for health gain.

Reflections

After the series of learning set meetings was completed participants were asked to reflect on the usefulness and transferability of the process from their point of view. There was a universal view that the learning set process was an effective means of developing a deeper and shared understanding of the perspectives and constraints of different agencies, and that this in turn provided an essential baseline for establishing a greater awareness of the possibilities for commissioning health-promoting services and working towards health improvement. Many lessons which were transferable to local situations had been acquired through the process of working with other committed people who were interested, but also properly 'disinterested' so that they could offer non-partisan advice and comment, and together 'model' effective multi-agency working. Many participants referred to the building of a climate of trust and honesty with the learning set such that it was possible to explore ideas and develop new solutions with safety and confidence. There is no doubt that participants have already gained substantially from their involvement in the learning sets, that these gains have already affected their commissioning behaviour and, for many, there is still a 'rich harvest to be reaped' for the future.

The main areas of impact were as follows:

- Contributions to personal, professional and organisational development:

  - Very many participants mentioned the fact that they had gained a better understanding of others' roles and organisations. This was particularly the case between health and local government, but also applied between different roles and organisations within the health service such as primary care, public health, and acute and community commissioning.

  - Learning of this kind often then gave participants the confidence, reassurance and determination to pursue (or continue to pursue) practical routes towards multi-agency health improvement. In sum there was evidence of transferable in-depth understanding of other agencies' roles, responsibilities and aspirations.

  - Whilst acknowledging that time is a precious resources for all participants, there were many references to the value of taking time to reflect, to enjoy the exposure to new ideas, and to clarify concepts and thinking.

  - The value of networking was mentioned many times. Here the important outcomes were a realisation that others shared the same problems, were willing to work together in a non-judgemental way that provided both support and challenge, and that it was possible to explore cultural differences with safety. People valued the quality and engagement of their fellow participants and expected to maintain networks and friendships.

Everyone placed a strong emphasis and value on the multi-agency dimension, using terms such as 'crucial' and 'vital'. It was described as a 'unique opportunity' but 'not cosy, real trust had to be built', and 'much more valuable than other formats'.

Particular strengths of the format were seen to be:

- The quality, commitment and enthusiasm of group members and their geographical and professional spread.

- The quality of the facilitation, creating a relaxed, honest and open environment and providing useful theory and information.

- The logical, flowing and self-determined agenda.

All learning sets can be ranged along a continuum (Figure 14) from 'fluid' to 'structured' in terms of the extent to which the agenda is developed 'live' by the group or consists of a series of pre-determined sessions.

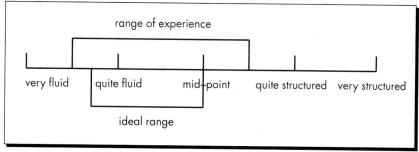

Fig. 14. A learning set continuum

We asked participants where they thought their learning set should be placed on this continuum in practice, and ideally where it should be. The balance of *fluid/structured* in the format of the learning set emerged as appropriate to the task and participants' needs.

In order to assess further whether this format was effective, participants were also asked whether they felt they could have achieved the same gains by other routes and, informally, whether they themselves felt they represented a good investment. The answer to this second question was (after a slightly shocked silence!) emphatically 'yes', given the very substantial resources they controlled. The answer to the first question was rather more variable. While many thought this was the only or best way, with comments such as 'this learning set where we structured our own programme worked extremely well', others who were less certain still said they found it difficult to imagine a 'course' which met the same objectives, or remarked 'I can only think of time-consuming, expensive conferences'.

Given the choice most people would prefer to invest their time and energy in this form of development. One person said 'this is particularly suitable for adults – with a real commitment to coming up with real solutions', another that it represented both a high-risk and high-gain form of learning.

From learning to practice

Participants were asked what they were already doing or planning to do differently as a consequence of their involvement in the learning sets. This included:

● Reducing isolation and gaining perspective by being able to inform local colleagues about what was happening on a wider front.

● Being sharper about determining outcomes and processes for health gain, and becoming more pragmatic about possibilities whilst also realising how many opportunities in fact exist.

● Realising how important it is to work at understanding different organisational cultures in order to achieve the partnership agenda.

- Using models of change that were explored in the learning set to plan social services–primary care changes across a city.

- Involving primary health services in CHD prevention to a greater extent.

- Involving other agencies at an early stage and on a continual basis to review progress against health priorities, and focusing more clearly on priority setting.

Participants were also asked to consider ways in which the learning set format should be taken forward in the future, including the extent to which it was feasible or desirable to contemplate local versions.

There was a strong balance towards feeling that 'too local' versions might be difficult to make work, except perhaps in areas where joint working was already well developed. If it were to work it would need to be, at minimum, well-facilitated and on neutral ground.

The arguments against local versions of the learning set were:

- They would probably provide fewer good opportunities for new thinking and innovation because people know each other too well and may therefore tend to act on the basis of preconceived ideas and stereotypes.

- Local politics and 'hidden agendas' are likely to inhibit shared openness and honesty, and could become 'problem-hindering' groups, unwilling to let go of constraints.

- Simple physical proximity could encourage dropping in and out and reduce commitment.

However, some people felt that a regional version might well represent an acceptable middle ground between local and national. Certainly there is potential for substantial gains to be made through these means, as it becomes easier for key individuals to recognise that the 'system' is not as inflexible as it may sometimes seem.

6. The health gain consultancy programme

Design

This programme was designed for experienced health promotion professionals in England to enable them to explore new ways to manage the health promotion agenda effectively in a complex and changing world. This focus was complemented by a commitment to helping the managers involved develop personal learning skills and new capabilities.

The foundation of the programme was a recognition that health promotion skills and knowledge are becoming increasingly central to NHS strategy. This is a reflection not only of a value-for-money imperative but also an emphasis on effectiveness and outcomes in the planning and delivery of health services. The move towards a more explicit focus on health gain, as a key performance indicator, led us to believe that health promotion professionals have a great deal to offer and contribute to the continuing achievement of this.

At the heart of the programme was a recognition of the potential evolution of health promotion professionals from direct service providers and managers, advisers and development specialists (particularly in commissioning and purchasing activities) to health gain consultants. This entails using the skills they already have, but linking them more broadly with the tools and techniques of organisation development. In this way health promotion professionals will be able to bring about real change by working inter- and intra-organisationally. The health gain consultancy programme in developing these ideas, provided a group of health promotion professionals with the opportunity to redefine their role, and identify the skills, abilities and knowledge they will need to manage this transition.

Participants on the programme were drawn from a range of NHS organisations, including purchasers and providers. To gain access to the programme, participants had to be nominated by their chief executives and then pass through a paper-based selection process managed by the HEA. Fifteen people started the programme in January 1996.

The outline programme was designed by members of the Joint Venture in conjunction with leading health promotion managers. The key aim was to provide access to high level development and at the same time to ensure that a pragmatic sense of realism pervaded the programme content. The programme was designed to link theory and practice, provide tailor-made case studies, appropriate expert input, draw on excellent practice from the field and other public, private and voluntary services and make use of participants' own experience of working in and managing health promotion.

Participants were actively encouraged to influence the design of the programme. This included making suggestions about the content of future modules (Figure 15). Mid-programme reviews were an integral part of each module. The focus of these was on both content issues – what was being delivered and worked on – and on process issues – how participants were working together collectively as a learning community. This openness on the part of the tutors and group members required a subtle balancing on everyone's part in order to ensure that the agreed programme curriculum could be delivered and that, at the same time, the individual and collective requests of group members could also be met.

The programme lasted a total of 20 days and comprised an introductory two-day session; four four-day modules; and a final review and evaluation session of two days. The two-day introductory session had two main purposes. First, to identify where health promotion was currently located within the NHS and second, to 'develop the group' such that it could become a sustainable 'learning community' for the lifetime of the programme.

The module themes along with brief details of their content are listed in Figure 15.

- **Module 1: Mapping the environment for change**
  An exploration of future scenarios for health services and the role and location of health promotion within them.
  Mapping stakeholders for the new NHS and their relative power and influence to lead and manage change.
  Local Agenda 21, anti-poverty and regeneration.
  Organisational trends, new management and leadership.
  Social market theory and the implications of this for health.

- **Module 2: Shaping commissioning**
  Evidence-based health promotion.
  Consultancy skills and organisational change.
  Commissioning for health – the primary care-led NHS.

- **Module 3: From health promotion to health gain**
  Future patterns – planning health strategies and the move to health gain.
  Organisation development skills and techniques.
  Managing and working in a political environment.
  Making health strategies work – working in partnership.

- **Module 4: Achieving health gain**
  Social marketing for health promotion.
  User involvement in the commissioning for health gain.
  Project management.
  Shifting the balance of care – individual empowerment and social change.

Fig. 15: The themes for modules plus brief details of their content

Each module in the programme contained at least three evening sessions. These included sessions led by participants and by members of the core tutor group. There was also a programme dinner to which outside speakers were invited. Visiting speakers included: the chief executive of a national homelessness agency who explored the links between homelessness and health gain; an external consultant who talked about the consultancy role and processes; and members of the HEA and OPM who talked about areas of their work practices in which the group had expressed interest.

Content and process

Throughout the delivery of the programme, the aims were to make the issues addressed 'come alive' and be authentic and real for the participants; to have the programme content located within participants' current experience; and at the same time extend this into potential futures for their role and profession. Below are descriptions of two of the modules to provide a flavour of the programme as a whole.

Future strategies for health

The group was given copies of scenarios for the year 2007.[14] (This consisted of two versions of the 'future' developed by OPM through a 'Delphi' process.) Participants were each allocated a particular 'future' prior to the module and asked to spend time talking through the implications of this with colleagues and co-workers; in essence to use the scenario material as environmental data and to consider the implications for health services.

During the module the group was introduced to ideas and processes for strategy development. The group was then split into two, based on which scenario they had been working with, and asked to prepare strategies for the health service in 2007, with a particular focus on the role for health promotion and health gain. To help support this process, and provide an 'external voice', three professionals, from outside the group, were invited to provide commentary on the final presentations. Our external panel of professionals was: Howard Shaw, Deputy Director of Research and Development, West Midlands Executive; Julia Unwin, Visiting Fellow at OPM and special adviser to NatWest Bank and the Baring Foundation; and Marcia Saunders, Assistant Director of Social Services, London Borough of Havering.

Each group made their presentation and then entered into dialogue with the panel. One group proposed a highly developed notion of joint commissioning with health and local government submerged within a new body supported by elected representatives. The outcomes of the process were fairly convergent, which was interesting given the divergent nature of the two scenarios.

The group said they had found the exercise quite difficult, as a result of what they experienced as the negative aspects of both scenarios, with group members' energy being 'sapped' by the difficulties they felt that they would experience if either scenario were to fully come about. The panel's reflections and challenges to the group were most sharply focused on this capacity of people to be 'frozen' by difficulties, rather than using periods of uncertainty as a chance to assert themselves and their professions. A key skill at such times is that of 'managing up', that is, moving an issue on to others' agendas and finding new ways of working that both meet the needs of the service and service users.

Managing and working in a political environment

The focus of this module was helping participants to develop their capacity to work in both big and small 'political' situations. Prior to the session, participants were asked to identify and write up work-based political dilemmas they had experienced, or were currently experiencing. These could be of any 'political' nature (big or small). They were asked to send them to the programme manager at OPM, who spent time anonymising them.

During the module participants were introduced to the work of Baddeley and James[15] as a way of exploring these dilemmas and how to manage them more effectively. Baddeley and James propose a framework for helping managers work with overtly and covertly political issues. This framework is based upon the notion that the effective manager has a capacity to read an organisation or situation. He or she is able to work out what is going on and any of the consequences of the action, thereby managing the dilemma rather than being managed by it. At the same time managers know when they are acting in an authentic manner rather than being pulled towards game playing, or ego defensive behaviour. The group used this framework to explore the dilemmas they had originally prepared, considering different responses dependent upon the individual's capacity to 'read' what was going on and managing different degrees of authenticity.

The dilemmas submitted included examples of conflicting agendas within the workplace as a result of differences of race, gender and sexuality and also the ethical issues relating to gathering sponsorship for programmes and managing the influence of sponsors who may wish to 'skew' the health gain message in a particular direction.

A presentation by Diana McInnes, from the Department of Health, provided participants with an insider's guide to the department. The aim was to help them increase their capacity to 'read' at a policy level. The day concluded with an in-depth consideration of the role and place of values and ethics in the workplace. The challenge of this was 'how do we resist the pull towards instrumentalism, believing that the means justify the ends, and work in our practice and profession with integrity?'

Outcomes

Participants shaped the design of the closing two-day session with a focus on 'ending and beginnings'. The aim of this event was to provide ways of consolidating the learning, support the transfer of learning from the teaching environment to the world of work. During the two days, participants spent time on structured action planning, problem-solving and also on exploring ways of making firmer connections between their work in localities and the national role of the HEA.

A final stream of activity focused on writing up accounts of the experience of becoming a health gain consultant. Two key strands emerged from this:

- defining what a health gain consultant does;

- what changes within the NHS would support the development of this role.

All the participants expressed their enthusiastic appreciation at having been able to take the time, and to use the space the programme provided, to undertake supported reflection on their personal practice as health promotion professionals. This had enabled them to use the programme collectively and individually to develop new definitions of their role and practice as health promotion professionals. In essence, the programme provided the time and space to move away from the day-to-day and identify some of the bigger, more strategic issues that need to be addressed.

The issue of 'unifying threads' was raised by participants. It was at times hard for the participants, once involved in module activities, to recognise the key ideas connecting the activities together. This would at times only become apparent after the programme had ended. This is to be expected in longer programmes where the participants are dealing both with the world as it is and at the same time exploring the potential for future development within a profession or practice. Participants need to have the capacity to handle a high degree of ambiguity to separate out what is part of the future and what is a given for now. As tutors it is our responsibility to help with this process, and encourage participants to locate the dilemmas they are encountering within their own practice, and provide supportive ways of managing these. Participants reported that once they had made the connection between themselves, and their organisation with regard to programme content, wider explorations of health promotion, and the potential for health gain consultancy within the NHS became possible.

The programme was experienced as both supportive and yet appropriately challenging. The style and approach to facilitation helped with this, as did the commitment to working with participants to shape it to meet their needs. The programme strengthened participants' commitment to seeing the achievement of health gain as not only through working within the NHS but also with other key public and voluntary sector agencies. Participants felt that the measures used to define what constitutes health gain need to have a broader base than those of traditional health promotion and education, and health gain was given a wide definition that included the mobilisation of the positive influences of physical, social and environmental factors that make a contribution to health and wellbeing. Generally, such measures have been based on changes in behaviour. There may also be the need for an acceptance that given the relatively small amounts of money spent on health promotion it is pointless to attempt to measure every last intervention for its outcomes. Health gain consultants need to find ways of joining the debate about effectiveness and influence the direction in which this is going. Measures of effectiveness need to appropriately reflect good practice.

It was seen as extremely useful to spend time defining and describing how a primary care-led NHS may develop and to ensure that opportunities are taken to make health gain central to this. This also included a realisation that many

NHS professionals are currently grappling with the evolution of their practice in this way and considering how they can contribute to the emergence of new ways of working. It was felt that the time is now right to exert wider influence to help shape the future. Health promotion professionals have the opportunity to develop models of good practice that can be promoted within the wider NHS. In particular it was felt that the time was now right for building closer and more effective links with public health specialists.

In many settings, health promotion professionals have already been working on a consultancy basis. Individual professionals and their organisations need to find ways of recognising these and to consciously develop them. The shift from health promotion specialist to health gain consultant is a transfer of skills, rather than a wholesale re-education of the profession.

The group identified the following key themes and offered them as a way forward for health promotion specialists and agencies to work together to inform the debate:

● The debate needs to be opened up to a wider audience.

● Current sources of evidence need to be critically assessed and alternatives sought and explored.

● New criteria need to be agreed for the appropriate assessment of evidence for health promotion interventions.

● Time to review available information needs to be built into work programmes.

● National and local research and development programmes need to link together to develop a more complete database of information and evidence.

● There is a need for the development of a more consistent range of outcome measures and indicators for the profession.

● The debate about such things as evidence needs to be kept in perspective. It is currently flavour of the month, but that might change.

A key strand during the programme was on the exploration of relationships between the HEA and people working in localities. Participants felt that working as part of the Joint Venture had enabled them to gain a clearer understanding of the roles and responsibilities of the HEA and also to develop new forms of working and collaborating together. At the same time they felt that they had been able to represent appropriately the dilemmas they faced at a local level; in particular the balancing of local needs demands against national expectations and standards.

Overall the programme has helped to highlight and engender a positive sense of the future for health promotion within the NHS.

References

1 Williams, R. *International Developments in Health Care: A Review of Health-Care Systems in the 1990s.* Royal College of Physicians, 1995.

2 NHS Executive. *Developing NHS Purchasing and GP Fundholding: Towards a Primary Care-led NHS.* January 1995.

3 NHS Executive. *An Accountability Framework for GP Fundholding,* EL(94)79. April 1995.

4 Department of Health. *Choice and Opportunity – Primary Care: The Future.* HMSO, October 1996.

5 Welsh Office/NHS Directorate. *Strategic Intent and Direction for the NHS in Wales.* Welsh Health Planning Forum, 1989.

6 Welsh Office/NHS Directorate. *The Welsh Health Planning Forum: Protocol for Investment in Health Gain – Cancers.* Welsh Office, December 1990.

7 *The Health of the Nation: a Strategy for Health in England,* Cm 1986. HMSO, 1992.

8 Quoted in Simnett, I. *Managing Health Promotion: Developing Healthy Organisations and Communities.* Wiley, 1995.

9 Griffiths, R. Health gain 'triumphs' in *Heath Gain '92: The Standing Conference.* Office for Public Management, 1992.

10 NHS Executive. *Priorities and Planning Guidance for the NHS 1996/7,* EL(96)45. 1996.

11 *Chameleon: Commissioning for Health Gain.* Health Education Authority and Office for Public Management, 1995.

12 Professor R. Balarajan at the NHS Ethnic Health Unit/NAHAT conference in Harrogate on 20 June 1996, referring to research to be published shortly.

13 *What the Doctor Ordered – a Study of GP Fundholders in England & Wales.* Audit Commission, May 1996.

14 *The Future of Public Services – 2007.* Office for Public Management, July 1995.

15 Baddeley, S. and James, K. Owl, fox, donkey or sheep: political skills for managers. *Management Education and Development,* vol. 18, 1987, pp. 3–19.

Appendix: Participants

The following were all contributors to the Joint Venture.

Roundabout simulation

Simulation director
Jeff Rodrigues
Office for Public Management

Moderators
Helen Brown
Office for Public Management
Graham Coomber
NHS Executive, West Midlands

Rapporteurs
Bernie Evans
Health Education Authority
Peter Martin
Office for Public Management

Simulation administrators
Trudi Coope
Office for Public Management
Lorraine Finegan
Office for Public Management

The Players
Linda Aston
Lichfield Street Practice, Walsall
Anju Bhabuta
Health Education Authority
Anne Bishop
*Midlands Family Practice,
West Midlands*
Kevin Conod
The Limes Medical Centre, Walsall
Tracy Conod
The Limes Medical Centre, Walsall
Alan Dean
Sandwell Social Services
W. Denys
Northgate Medical Centre, Walsall

Roger Fessey
*Sandwell Health Authority,
West Midlands*
Peter Forrester
Coventry Health Authority
R. K. Griffiths
NHS Executive, West Midlands
Chris Howgrave-Graham
Coventry Health Authority
Amanda Killoran
Health Education Authority
Helen King
Health Education Authority
David Lye
NHS Executive, West Midlands
Ian McComiskie
Dudley Priority NHS Trust
Paul Norman
Multifund, Birmingham
Peter O'Brien
The Forest Medical Group, Coventry
Sam Ramaiah
Walsall Health
Ina Simnett
Health Promotion Consultant
Andrew Snookes
Sandwell Community Health Council
Jean Spray
Health Education Authority
Wendy Taylor
NHS Executive, West Midlands
Russell Tipson
Action Heart, Wellesley House
Alan Towers
BBC, Pebble Mill
Simon Walford
Royal Wolverhampton Hospitals
Rose Wheeler
Office for Public Management
Dawn Wickham
West Bromwich Health

Research – Health promotion and health gain in a primary care-led NHS

Researchers and Project managers
Anju Bhabuta
Health Education Authority
Jeff Rodrigues
Office for Public Management

Action learning sets
Facilitators
Helen Brown, Liz Haggard,
Christine Kent
Office for Public Management

Participants
Rifat Atun
Woodford Fundholding Consortium
Ian Ayres
South West London Total Purchasing Programme
Isobel Bowler
Wandsworth Borough Council
Carole Brown
Derby City Consortium
Sven Bunn
Merton, Sutton and Wandsworth Health
Pat Dark
NHS Executive, South Thames
Paul Edmonson-Jones
West Sussex Health Authority
Peter Elliott
Redbridge and Waltham Forest Health Authority
Karen Ford
Health Education Authority
Richard Foulger
London Borough of Bromley
Amelia Garman
Brighton Borough Council
Peter Greagsby
Rotherham Health Authority
Alison Hamilton
Dudley Health
Ian Hammond
Hillingdon Health Agency
Veronica Kirk
Southern Derbyshire Health

Terry Lawrence
NHS Executive, West Midlands
Judi Linney
West Surrey Health Commission
Hugh Maclean
Fleming House Medical Centre
Jean Mallett
Essex County Council
Debra Pattinson
Braintree District Council
Becky Pollard
Suffolk Health
Ian Powell
City of Coventry
Jill Stannard
Southampton & S. W. Hants Health
Carolyn Stephenson
Newcastle Social Services Department
Ronald Turner
West London Health Promotion
Richard Watson
St Helens and Knowsley Health
Les Woods
Local Government Management Board

The health gain consultancy programme

Programme managers
Robin Douglas
Office for Public Management
Bernie Evans
Health Education Authority
Ian Gee
Office for Public Management
Dominic Harrison
Consultant to the Health Education Authority
Jean Spray
Health Education Authority

Participants
Stuart Bentley
South Staffordshire Health Authority
Paul Butcher
St Mary's Hospital, Leeds
Michael Calverley
Directorate of Health Promotion, Stoke on Trent

Charlotte Dale
Quest Health Promotion Service
Maggie Davies
Health Action, Weald of Kent Community NHS Trust
Pauline Davis
Nottingham Community Health
Louise Dunn
North Yorkshire Specialist Health Promotion Service
John Grigg
North Worcestershire Health Authority
Frankie Lynch
Health First, Lambeth Lewisham & Southwark

Sharma Sharif
Walsall Health
Alison Taylor
Enfield and Haringey Health Agency
Stan Thompson
Bromley Health
Geoff Wallis
Kensington, Chelsea and Westminster Health Commission
Jude Williams
East London & The City Health Promotion
Maureen Wiskin
North Staffordshire Health Authority